E. D. Michael

THE LAST
APPALACHIAN WOLF

THE LAST APPALACHIAN WOLF

EDWIN DARYL MICHAEL

quarrier press

DEDICATION

This historical novel is dedicated to my sons, Judd and Sean, who have been such valuable elements of the Michael pack.

ACKNOWLEDGMENTS

I am deeply indebted to the many individuals who provided advice, encouragement, and historical information during the period this novel was being prepared. The Allegheny Regional History Society, Beverly Heritage Center, and Randolph County Historical Society were extremely cooperative in researching specific historical events. Keith Inskeep provided information concerning the early days of the sheep industry in West Virginia and Frank Jernejcic provided information about the Cheat River and it's various Cheat Mountain tributaries. Bill Gillespie made me aware of the newspaper account of the last known timber wolf in the Appalachians. Julie Dzaack, Ken Dzaack, Norman Julian, and Kathy Leo graciously edited early drafts. Jim Anderson, Christopher Stewart, and Paul Ludrosky were instrumental in obtaining wolf photographs.

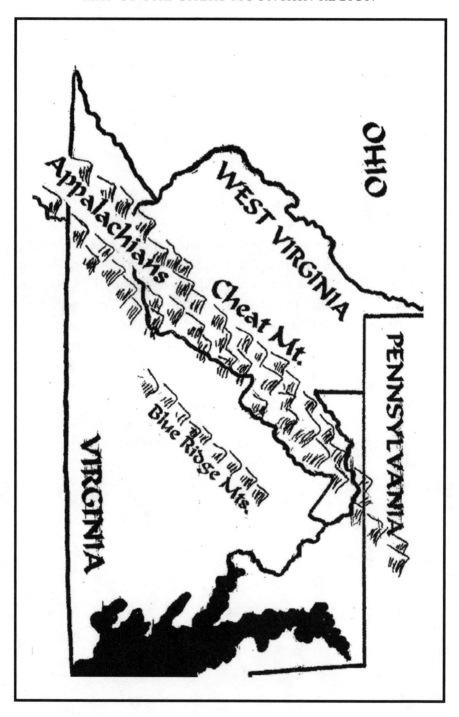

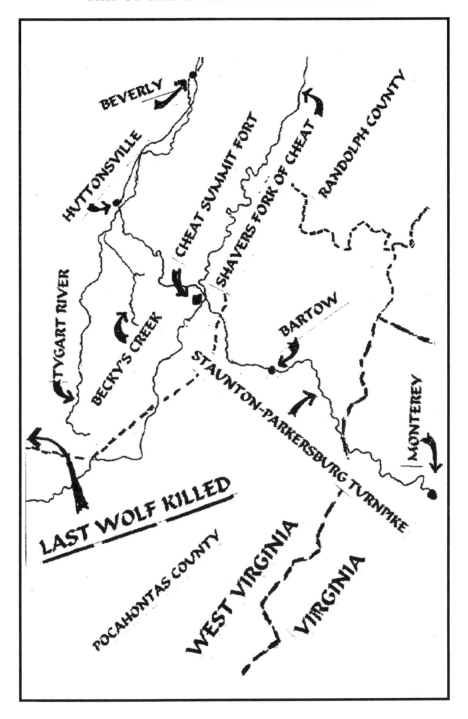

Quarrier Press
Charleston, WV

Copyright 2014 by Edwin D. Michael

10 9 8 7 6 5 4 3 2 1

Library of Congress Control Number: 2014-937984
ISBN 13: 978-1891852-95-4
ISBN 10: 1-891852-95-7

Original watercolor cover illustration: Jason Queen
Layout and Cover design: Jason Queen

Printed in USA

Distributed by:

1125 Central Avenue
Charleston, WV 25302
www.wvbookco.com

TABLE OF CONTENTS

ᘒ *PREFACE* ᘖ

West of the Atlantic Ocean, west of the broad coastal plain, west of that Great Valley of Virginia known as Shenandoah, and west of the hazy mountains named the Blue Ridge lies an even taller range of blue and hazy mountains. These are the Appalachians "the endless mountains" and their story is one of eons past and of many now-forgotten changes to its ecosystems.

This, the oldest of mountain ranges in North America and possibly the oldest on Earth at over 400 million years, stretches over 2,000 miles in a north-by-northeast direction from Alabama to Newfoundland, and once towered 16,000 feet above the sea. Humans, at various times in the distant past, designated sections of the Appalachian range as distinct entities, although in some cases it is difficult to determine where one section ends and another begins. Cumberland, Great Smoky, Blue Ridge, Catoctin, Adirondack, Allegheny, Catskill, Berkshire, Green, White, and Schickshock were names assigned to select sections of the Appalachians by early European settlers and the explorers who preceded them.

One particular section in the midriff of the great Appalachian chain was given the name "Cheat" by some unknown trader or trapper or settler who ventured into this vast wilderness. The basis for this term has long been forgotten. Some believe it refers to the nutrient-poor grasses prevalent on the mountaintops that "cheated" livestock by providing little, if any, energy. Others believe it was named for the severe weather so characteristic of these mountains—cheating man out of his life. Another origin centered on the name of an early explorer, La Cheath, the first European to travel the many rivers draining this highland region.

In the early 1700s the Appalachian Mountains teemed with a long-forgotten array of wildlife, including that most complex of North American predators, the timber wolf. But by 1890 this icon of the great eastern wilderness had disappeared from all portions of the Appalachians except one—the Cheat Mountain region of what is now West Virginia.

This historical treatise portrays the distant and forgotten interactions of wolves and humans in the violent and unforgiving landscape of the Cheat Mountains, along with the unfortunate outcome that is now history.

ෙ CHAPTER ONE ෴
CHEAT MOUNTAIN IN 1750

The deep-throated howl of an adult timber wolf rolled eerily across the summit of Cheat Mountain. Every deer and elk within hearing range instantly became alert and directed their attention towards the howl. The howl was repeated once, and then once again. To the hoofed animals residing in the Cheat Mountain region, the call echoed similar to hundreds of other howls throughout the year that announced the presence of their primary predator. But to five wolves on a hunting expedition four miles away, alarm and a hint of fear were recognizable in the deep resonating call. The pack halted its deadly pursuit of a white-tailed deer doe and silently concentrated on the alarm howls. Each wolf of the hunting party immediately recognized the voice as that of the adult female wolf who had remained on guard at the pack's semi-permanent, summer "encampment" along with two yearling females and a flurry of pups.

This site, on an elevated knoll and within view of a small tributary of the Cheat River, was the second home the five pups had known. Their first three weeks of life had been spent in the hillside den where they were born, but soon afterwards the pups were taken by their mother to the pack's encampment site. Crowding, general unsanitary conditions, and a desire to avoid the fleas and ticks were reasons enough for the mother to move her nearly-weaned young to the fresh air and fresh earth of the elevated knoll. All other pack members had readily accepted the abandonment of the nursery den—an annual ritual—and adopted the knoll as the pack's summer headquarters, or "rendezvous" site. These were eastern timber wolves, *Canis lupus*, also known as gray wolves.

"Canus", the alpha male, replied to his mate's alarm howls with an even deeper howl, and all wolves in the hunting party quietly waited for a response from the female at the encampment site. Within minutes, the hunting pack received the female's message. Danger was present! There were only a few threats that would have triggered such a near-panic call as the one broadcast by the lead female. A marauding black bear was one possibility. But with the wolf pups nearly six months old, and quite capable of escaping into an underground den or even outrunning a bear, this event would normally not have triggered such a frantic howl. A hunting party of Indians would have elicited silence rather than alarm howls. With no knowledge of what the danger might be, the alpha male yipped a command to his pack and all immediately set off at a ground-eating gallop back toward their den site.

"Verde", the experienced, eight-year old female, had been the first to detect the alien odor feared by all wildlife—an odor threatening death for all animals not capable of flying, swimming, or burrowing deep within the protective earth. Smoke!

Smoke, and its accompanying fire, was an annual occurrence in the mountains. The Cheat Mountain wolf pack had lost three members to fire during the previous decade, and four others carried permanent scars where hair had been severely singed. As had their ancestors for thousands of years, all wolves in the pack recognized and reacted to the danger inherent in this serious threat.

In less than 20 minutes the main pack returned to the rendezvous site, and during much face-licking Canus, the alpha male, and Verde, the alpha female, communicated in the manner perfected by their species throughout generations. They had two options: rapidly return to the den site where they could retreat deep within the maze of tunnels, or flee the area. Barely two years before they had attempted to flee from an oncoming fire and lost two pups. When smoke burned their eyes, the pups had ignored the frantic yelps of the adults, ran towards the fire, and suffocated.

A pack of adult wolves could typically outrun a forest fire. On a dry, hot day with a brisk afternoon breeze pushing the fire across the mountain, however, the flames would travel faster than the canines. With awkward, independent-minded pups, the danger was great and the threat of death obvious. The wolves had no way of knowing the intensity of the fire or the direction it was traveling. Had the entire pack been several miles from the den site they would have fled, and most likely escaped danger. However, parental care and total pack devotion are extremely strong in timber wolves. As the smoke became stronger the pups were the first to suffer. Stinging eyes forced them to whimper and run in wild circles, attempting to avoid the unseen hazard. The decision was quickly made. Adults would defend pups of the pack against black bears or mountain lions, often fighting to the death. They would never abandon their pups.

The alpha female led the pack back to the den where the pups had been born six months earlier. The pups anxiously sought the familiar safety of the cavity where they had spent hundreds of carefree hours. The adults followed the pups into the cool tunnels. However, retreat into the farthest depths of the tunnel maze did not guarantee comfort and survival. The tunnel maze contained several entrances, and thus smoke could be drawn into and through the den. If the fire passed rapidly overhead there would be little opportunity for smoke to be sucked into the dens. But if it were a slow-moving fire, oxygen would be pulled out of the den as smoke was pulled in.

This particular late-summer fire had been intentionally set by a band of nine Iroquois returning from a trading expedition to the Shenandoah Valley and coastal Virginia. For hundreds of years, Indians had been setting fire to the forests and grassy "balds" that blanketed the Appalachian Mountains. Their original goal had been to clear dense underbrush and thus facilitate travel. However, roving hunting parties were quick to recognize that deer, elk, and buffalo (currently referred to as bison) concentrated in those areas where succulent grasses were the most abundant. And blackened tree trunks were testament to the fires that gave rise to the lush grasses on those particular hillsides.

Even without the assistance of Indians, fires occurred annually throughout the Appalachians. Lightning strikes on dried grasses and leaves of late summer annually ignited several "natural" fires. The accumulation of dead limbs, spruce needles, moss, and humus under the red spruce stands reached 1-2 feet thick and fueled a hot ground fire when flames invaded. Fire's periodic removal of compacted litter and the subsequent release of nutrients created excellent seedbeds. With the arrival of warm spring rains, the sun-lit openings and the forest floor suddenly metamorphosed from the drab browns of winter into vibrant blankets of green. There was a sudden emergence of energy over the mountainous landscape, as the earth once again showcased its great wealth of life.

Green was good! For the grazers, a verdant landscape meant greater quality and quantities of available plant foods. For the predators (human and wildlife), a green landscape identified hunting grounds where opportunities to locate potential prey were significantly higher than in surrounding forests. Rich swaths of grasses meant fat animals, and lots of them.

❧ *CHAPTER TWO* ❧
DEADLY SMOKE

Although no permanent Indian settlements existed in the Cheat Mountains during the 1700s, numerous hunting parties visited the region every autumn. White-tailed deer and elk were abundant throughout the higher elevations and small herds of buffalo frequented river valleys. This was quite a contrast to the conditions east of the mountains.

Game animals had been depleted in the immediate vicinity of most permanent Indian settlements throughout land lying between the Atlantic Ocean and the central Appalachians. While Native Americans recognized that periodic over hunting would lead to a drastic decline in wildlife, they were forced to hunt within the areas around their permanent settlements. The natives were also drawn to distant hunting grounds that would provide a sustainable source of meat if they harvested only the "surplus"—the annual production. Thus each tribe protected its own territorial hunting grounds, many located hundreds of miles from its permanent settlement. Planned burns within those remote hunting grounds resulted in greater numbers of game animals.

Utilizing flint and steel, the nine Iroquois men had effortlessly ignited the dried grasses and leaves at more than 30 spots along a meandering line nearly 100 yards in length. Confident in their

5

abilities to set effective fires, they had moved on in moments, having triggered the important cycle of changes. Wearing only leather moccasins, leggings, and loincloths, the Iroquois quickly shouldered their packs and continued on northward in the mild summer weather.

Initially, the light breeze out of the north pushed the fire slowly southward. But, by mid-afternoon the wind had accelerated and the fire was burning a swath almost one-half mile wide. Upwind from the flames, the Iroquois smiled with satisfaction, as they looked southward from atop a rocky promontory and admired the towering plumes of smoke a mile away. Intense flames consumed grasses and shrubs in treeless areas. In stands of chestnut and oak flames did little damage to the trees, many of which had thick, fire-resistant bark. Stands of conifers were less resistant. Resins in the needles of hemlock, balsam fir, and red spruce were ideal fuel. Those particular evergreen trees exploded in flames, often throwing sparks high into the swirling, fire-created winds. The fire pulsed rapidly and hungrily across the high peaks of Cheat Mountain, lingering or fading as fuels allowed.

The Iroquois would return to this landscape in autumn of the following year, when mornings would be frosty, grasses would be tall, elk would be fat, and hunting would be successful. Hundreds of pounds of smoked meat would be packed in baskets for transport to their permanent camp in northern Pennsylvania.

As their fire spread rapidly southward, the Indians knew nothing of the wolf pack that sought shelter in the depths of a convoluted den complex. The Iroquois would have had no concerns or regrets at the threat facing the wolves' survival. Fewer wolves meant more elk.

With considerable whining and squirming the pups had sought the security of Verde, their mother. But there was little she could do to protect them from the smoke that slowly crept into the den complex. The largest of the pups, a dark gray male, forced his siblings aside and thrust his nose into his mother's sheltering fur.

"Lupa", the dark gray alpha pup, had gained dominance in the litter through hundreds of mock fights, and now displayed considerable confidence. As a result of his dominance he always managed to consume more than his share of the meat brought to the den, and now weighed nearly five pounds more than his siblings. As wild fires burned overhead through grasses and blueberry bushes, one of his brothers attempted to push closer to their mother. Lupa responded with a growl and a sharp nip and retained the choice location at his mother's thick chest fur. After a few minutes of jostling for position the nervous pups napped, confident their mother would feed and protect them, just as she had their entire life.

For nearly half an hour the cool, fresh air of the den provided comfort to the mass of wolves, but slowly the damp air began to move. Drawn by the approaching heat, the shift in air temperature was only minutes ahead of the crackling sounds from above. Foreign, irritating smoke penetrated to the depths of the tunnel as the fire came overhead. A light gray female pup was the first wolf to panic. The smallest of her litter, the pup was regularly intimidated by her four littermates during their aggressive play. Now, they forced her from the mother wolf, and she was the first to suffer eye-stinging pain. She clamped her eyelids tight to cover her golden-yellow eyes, but to no avail.

Unable to understand or tolerate the hurt that had invaded her den, the pup instinctively scrambled to the den opening and sprinted in panic through the smoke—directly towards the flames. Unaware, she plunged headfirst into and then through the wall of flames. With eyes stinging and patches of fur burning, the pup screamed in agony. Running blindly, she bounded into a dense stand of mountain laurel and her momentum forced her deep into the thicket. The branches beat out most of the fire on the pup' fur and she was momentarily brought to a halt. She bit frantically at the pain near the tip of her tail and managed to extinguish the last of the burning fur.

The deadly line of flames and smoke progressed south of the den, and a fresh, exhilarating wind from the north was welcome relief. Nearly exhausted, the light gray female pup sought shelter among the roots of the laurel and curled into a ball. Whimpering in pain, she eventually entered a fitful sleep.

Fortunately for the remainder of the wolf pack, the fast-moving wind had pushed the flames past the den openings and prevented smoke from completely filling the tunnels. Although all the wolves suffered discomfort, all survived. As the wind exhausted the smoke from the den, they slowly emerged into a new world. First to appear was the alpha male, followed by the other adult wolves of the Cheat Mountain pack. Lupa, the large male pup, was the first of the pups to exit, but considerable calling by the mother wolf was required to persuade the other three pups to leave the safety of their den.

Once outside, the pups were greeted by acrid air and a foreign land. Tree trunks, blueberry bushes, azaleas, mountain laurels, defoliated conifers, and even boulders were now blackened. Lingering hot embers, flickering flames, and plumes of smoke attested to the destruction they had escaped. Unwilling to venture into this landscape, Canus forcibly herded his pack back to the security of their den. Frightened and confused, the wolf pack spent an uneasy night. Troubled by the absence of his sister, who had been his closest playmate, Lupa sent out barely audible, plaintive yips throughout the night. But there was no response. Had his leader not ordered the entire pack into the den complex Lupa would have ventured out in search of his missing sister.

As darkness cloaked the mountains, the injured female pup struggled back to the den. Painfully dragging her right front foot, which had been burned deeply, the struggling pup eventually located her pack. For the next hour the mother wolf licked her, and the pup was comforted. But the flames and acrid smoke had seared the pup's lungs, and as the sun eased over the mountain ridge to the east the pup lay lifeless among the awakening pack. Death was seldom easy in the wilderness.

❧ CHAPTER THREE ❧
A NEW DEN

One day after the fire, Canus led the pack from the birthing den. From a still-smoldering spruce log, a single tendril of smoke drifted upwards as if drawn towards the moon in the still-dark western sky. But irritating smoke had lifted and most of the ground underfoot had cooled. The wolves stretched, howled a few times, rubbed noses, licked faces, and reaffirmed the bonds that enabled the pack to function as a single social entity.

Lupa was the most inquisitive of the pups. Within the first hour he had managed to step on a still-glowing spruce stump and pull smoke into his lungs when he thrust his nose into a hole at the base of a birch tree. Next he discovered the blackened leg bone of an elk, which had been a plaything for the pups.

Around mid-day Canus signaled the others to follow, and they set off in single file towards a rendezvous site the pack had used eight years prior. Situated along the northern perimeter of the Cheat Mountain pack's home range, that specific den had been abandoned because a larger wolf pack had expanded its range to within one mile, much too close for the alpha male to tolerate. However, investigations made by Canus shortly before the fire had convinced him the larger wolf pack had, itself, abandoned the area. The lack of rival howling and the absence of territorial scent markings by other wolves convinced him that the area was not currently being used by other wolf packs.

Lupa and other individuals of the pack were spread out behind their leader in an orderly, single-file fashion as they began their journey. The leisurely travel north followed trails bordering the major stream draining that portion of the mountains. This stream, later to be named Shavers Fork (of the Cheat River), flowed through boreal forest similar to that dominating much of northern Canada. Slopes were lush with stands of red spruce, but also present were small pockets of balsam fir, aspen, beech, and red maple. Shrubby areas, characterized by mountain laurel, rhododendron, and azaleas were scattered among the conifer and hardwood stands.

Although much of Cheat Mountain consisted of steep slopes and narrow ridges, the area atop the mountain through which Shavers Fork flowed formed a relatively flat plateau. The ground was dense with moldering tree limbs and spongy mosses. Bogs, with carpets of cranberry vines, sphagnum mosses, and cottongrass were prevalent in those depressions where drainage was restricted throughout the Shavers Fork plateau. Hundreds of small mounds, each supporting viburnum bushes, pebbled the surface of every bog. Small streams meandered through several bogs. Scattered around the bogs were numerous open areas, the products of fires set by Iroquois in decades past. Short-term, the fires could have been viewed as a negative event for the land due to death and injury of both plants and animals. However, long-term, the fires had positive impacts on the overall biodiversity and health of the Cheat Mountain ecosystem.

❧ CHAPTER FOUR ❧
WOLF HISTORY

The lives of wolves and humans have been linked since groups of hunter-gatherers first roamed the steppes of Eurasia, tens of thousands of years ago. Most likely the two were originally competitors. Both competed for the carcass of any large mammal they might discover, whether one that died by accident or one that had been killed by a larger predator. As humans developed more sophisticated weapons and organized their hunts, their hunting prowess improved until they were frequently more successful than the wolves. A natural pattern, common in all of nature, emerged as lesser predators scavenged the carcasses abandoned by larger predators. As surely as ravens followed wolves, wolves began to follow humans.

Sometime after humans became efficient hunters, they began building semi-permanent settlements. Camp middens and landfills characterized every settlement, creating a new ecological niche that was recognized and utilized by wolves. Food items discarded by humans were consumed by those wolves brave enough to venture close to the settlements. Over time certain, less timid wolves became "camp followers." Eventually, a few of the more brazen wolves began stealthily entering camps at night, where they fed on bones and other items. Natural selection favored those assertive wolves having a greater tolerance of humans, and a commensal (both species benefit) relationship developed.

Wolves benefited from the food humans provided, and humans benefited from the wolves warning them of potential danger in the form of other predators and/or aggressive clans of other humans. Wolves had superior sight, smell, and hearing to that of humans. Eventually, through natural selection, certain wolves lost much of their natural fear of humans. The transformation was natural because both wolves and humans were social animals, hunting cooperatively to bring down prey much larger than themselves.

A logical outcome of wolves becoming camp followers was the birth of pups near human settlements. On many occasions wolf pups were captured by humans and hand-reared. Being social, wolf pups took readily to the clan way of life and melded easily into the daily routine. Surrogate parents, playmates, and alpha leaders naturally developed—a social arrangement not too different from what would have occurred in the wolf pack. Numerous other scavengers frequented camps of humans, but none became tame. Only wolves were pack animals that depended on a strong leader and obedient followers.

Through the thousands of years that hunter-gatherers wandered over Europe and Asia, a distinct type of wolf slowly evolved— one that would eventually become known as the "dog", the first animal domesticated by humans. This event occurred at various times and in numerous geographic locations, as semi-domestic "wolf-dogs" became civilized. Human hunters made the "wolf-dog" their ally. And both gained a companion that would be of comfort and security ever since.

Although the wolf-human relationship developed in Eurasia, the earliest known wolf ancestors first appeared in North America. Following their evolution in North America, these primitive wolves crossed the land bridge to Eurasia, where the large canid eventually obtained those features that characterize a modern-day wolf. Through several waves of re-colonization across the same land bridge, wolves returned to America where the species became widespread.

By the period when great glaciers covered much of the North American continent—approximately 10,000 years ago—timber wolves were the most widely distributed land animal in North America, and possibly the world. Wherever there were herds of large-hoofed mammals, there were wolves. Game rich, mixed deciduous-coniferous forests, such as those of Canada and the Appalachian Mountains, supported great numbers of wolves.

In the early 1700s the Cheat Mountain region of what is now West Virginia, a rugged area of some 500 square miles, supported as many as 15 large packs of wolves. Numbering upwards of 200 individuals, the packs and their territories were emblematic of the continent's astonishing numbers of wolves.

EDWIN DARYL MICHAEL

❧ *CHAPTER FIVE* ❧
LEARNING TO BE A WOLF

Lupa and the pack remained at their new den site for five days, during which time Canus, led several successful hunts into the surrounding areas. The beta female remained with the four pups at the den site, while Verde, the alpha female, and the other wolves of the pack accompanied Canus. The first hunt resulted in the successful kill of a large white-tailed doe. The adults fed ravenously, each consuming nearly ten pounds of venison. They leisurely returned to the den site, announcing their arrival a short distance away. Upon hearing the subdued howls, the pups anxiously emerged from the den, and engaged in wild, uninhibited play while awaiting the adults and the deer meat they were carrying.

Verde arrived first and was mobbed by the pups that had not eaten in three days. Lupa repeatedly licked and nipped at his mother's mouth and was rewarded with a regurgitated meal of fresh venison. The female created three other small piles approximately ten feet apart and plopped onto her side while her pups gulped down large pieces of deer.

When finished with their mother's contribution, the pups targeted Canus. Anxious licking and nipping around his mouth triggered the regurgitation of several additional small piles of meat. After one other adult contributed to the pups' feast, the adult female who had been babysitting begged a meal from one of the other adults. As darkness fell, the wolves selected individual sites the grass and in no time were sound asleep.

The daylight hours proved uneventful for the sleeping wolves and it was under the pink sky of dusk their pre-hunt ritual began. Lightning flashed in the east, but was so distant that no thunder was heard. Much face licking and joyous yipping occurred in anticipation of the upcoming hunt. Lupa and his siblings were allowed to join in the "hunt foreplay." This friendly get-together, which culminated in a chorus of howls, reinforced pack cohesiveness and, in some unknown manner, coordinated the hunt.

The howling chorus was typically initiated by one wolf. After the first or second dismal, wailing howl another wolf joined in. Eventually all members joined and a group howl developed. Such howls lasted 1-2 minutes, followed by a 15-20 minute quiet period. Howling occurrence was lowest in summer when pups were present. Peaks of howling occurred during breeding season in the spring.

Canus led his hunting companions back to the white-tailed deer carcass, but no meat remained. Foxes, weasels, and ravens had gleaned all the tidbits of flesh. The subsequent hunt was unsuccessful and the adults returned to the den. Hungry pups begged in vain, but it was not the first day they went without eating, and it would not be the last.

Eight days after introducing the pups to the new den, Verde led them to a knoll one-third of a mile away. This elevated point, overlooking a broad grassy glade along the Shavers Fork River, would function as the pack's rendezvous site for the next three months. The pups no longer required the security of a den and would spend most of their remaining lives aboveground. For the first week, an adult female remained with them while other members of the pack were hunting. But after that the pups were typically alone for entire nights.

With a surplus of energy, the pups seldom passed an hour of the day without engaging in some type of playful activity. Lupa was typically the leader and constantly stalked, chased, and wrestled his littermates. The silver-gray pup, whose blunt muzzle, large head, and stocky body contributed to his juvenile awkwardness, daily practiced his pouncing skills. Frequently he hid behind a tree or boulder in readiness to leap onto the back of one of his littermates. When the adults returned, their naps were constantly interrupted when Lupa pounced onto their twitching tail, or upon a flicking ear, or whatever body part tempted him at that moment. Weighing over 20 pounds, he was heavy enough to test the patience of the adults.

One sunny afternoon, as chickadees scolded overhead, Lupa pounced onto Canus' twitching hind leg and firmly clamped down with his small sharp baby teeth. Startled, Canus nipped Lupa on the neck and the pup went whimpering to his mother. This was only one of many valuable lessons that would lead to Lupa becoming an integral part of the pack.

Lupa and his siblings pounced on bones, feathers, and pieces of deer hide. They copied and learned from one another. They played tug-of-war with a piece of elk hide, strengthening their jaws and neck muscles. Their lessons became more advanced when they began wandering into the nearby bog. Pockets of standing water were present as were carnivorous sundews and interlaced strands of cranberries. The marsh grass was the home of meadow voles, shrews, salamanders, and snakes, all of which caused the grasses to wiggle and the wolf pups to become excited. Lupa pounced onto a small patch of wiggling grass early one morning and was surprised to find a squeaking vole trapped beneath one foot. A quick and mostly instinctual nip consummated the lesson with his first kill.

Little did Lupa and his siblings know that all this juvenile play was serious preparation for being successful adults. Hunting skills would develop simultaneously with bones and muscles. It was fun learning to be a wolf. And it was fun learning to howl. Lupa loved to howl. As a young pup, he had been the first of his litter to develop the skill. At two months, each whine became prolonged, eventually qualifying as a howl. Admittedly it was not much of a howl, more closely resembling a yip. But Lupa kept trying. So much so, that his mother nipped him on several occasions during daylight hours when he howled nearly nonstop. Yet by five months, his howling had matured and carried adult qualities.

Almost any occasion would prompt Lupa to howl. When the adults brought food back to the pups he howled. When he killed his first vole he howled. When he won a fight with one of his brothers he howled. One night, when all adults were away on a hunt, Lupa detected the distant howl of Canus. Recognizing it immediately, the pup elevated his snout, opened his mouth, and produced a fair rendition of a howl. He repeated it once, and once again.

Unfortunately for the pups, a black bear was slightly downwind and identified the caller as a youngster. The bear was an eight-year old male and had previous encounters with wolves. He approached, and waited for a sign that would reveal whether adults were present. When no adult were detected he advanced closer. In June, the bear had dug out a den of wolf pups, killing and eating two.

The rendezvous site where the wolf pups lived that summer had been chosen because it provided numerous dry sites for sleeping, proximity to water, and a broad open vista in three directions. Of greatest importance, it contained a dense stand of young red spruce and an even denser stand of rhododendron that would provide protective cover for the pups when the adults were away on a hunt.

Although a half moon lit the landscape, the black bear moving slowly through the spruce thicket was nearly invisible. As a feeble howl eased out of Lupa's mouth, the bear charged. He was less than ten yards away when Lupa detected him. The pup dashed in panic for the nearby rhododendron thicket and squeezed into the mass of tough stems and wrist-thick branches as the bear threw a potentially deadly swipe with one of its paws.

The mother wolf had taught the pups to seek shelter within the maze of rhododendron if any danger appeared. For creatures larger than a bobcat, a rhododendron thicket was more dense and impenetrable than any other plant cover on Cheat Mountain. Its limbs, so tough that they bent and splintered but rarely broke, would slow if not stop most hunters. The barrier brought the bear to a halt and provided time for

Lupa to move deeper into the dense tangle of stems and branches. Discouraged, the black bear abandoned Lupa and went in search of other food.

The well-learned lesson of retreat from the bear's attack had spared each pup's life. Lupa, however, learned something more, associating the bear's attack with his howling. It would be several days before he let his voice be heard again.

EDWIN DARYL MICHAEL

❧ CHAPTER SIX ☙
DANGEROUS PLAY

Lupa led his siblings on many excursions at night when adults were absent and during days when they were sleeping. Within days after arrival at the rendezvous site the pups were intimately familiar with every rock, log, chipmunk burrow, spruce tree, mushroom, and rhododendron thicket within 200 yards. The river was especially attractive. The Shavers Fork was no longer running high as it had during the spring. Summer months were an ideal time for wolf pups to learn about streams. The river was 70 feet wide and no more than two feet deep. Boulders and small rock outcrops tempted pups with steppingstones to venture away from the shoreline.

Lupa was the first to fall in. While digging into the sides of a beaver bank lodge he lost his balance and toppled into the river. The current was slow, but still swept him nearly 12 feet downstream before he regained his footing. Quickly jumping up onto the bank, he shook himself vigorously and immediately returned to the beaver lodge. During the days and nights that followed, the pups fearlessly ventured short distances into the river, but only belly deep. Although they could swim, they had no desire to do so.

Beaver, muskrats, mink, and other aquatic mammals swim before they walk. But to wolves, swimming is disconcerting and most are reluctant to enter water so deep their feet do not touch the bottom. Yet the abundance of aquatic animals was almost irresistible to the young wolves. Anything that moved drew their pursuit, and the five pups gained skills and calories as they captured fish, frogs, salamanders, and crawdads.

Most appealing to Lupa were the colorful and plentiful brook trout. Shavers Fork was near perfect habitat for brook trout. Cool, clear, highly oxygenated waters with gravelly bottoms provided the essential life requisites of these trout. The banks of the Shavers Fork River were tree-lined for long stretches, and many treetops tilted out over the river. Near constant shade meant water temperatures rarely exceeded 60 degrees. Lupa spent hours splashing through the shallow waters in pursuit of brook trout but never managed to capture one. He did discover the partially-eaten carcass of a large trout that had been captured by a river otter and the pup played with the bony prize on-and-off for an entire day. He chewed off small bites of the tasty raw flesh and spent hours gnawing on the head.

White-tailed deer and elk coming to the river to drink likewise attracted the pups' attention, but the young wolves did not know they were potential meals. The pups were more curious about the beaver and muskrat.

The agile river otter and the smaller mink were encountered almost daily, but the pups were neither predator nor prey to these mammals. Even adult wolves seldom killed an otter or mink unless it wandered some distance from the river. In the Shavers Fork River these two members of the weasel family had no enemies. Mink worked the shoreline and shallows, hunting frogs, crayfish, birds, and small rodents. These carnivores, nearly black when wet, would eat almost any prey they could capture. In contrast, the hunting efforts of river otters were aimed almost exclusively at fish. An adult otter, weighing up to 25 pounds, was capable of out swimming and killing any fish. Otters' aquatic skills were due in part to their webbed feet, and they could have easily attacked a wolf pup when it was in the water.

On one occasion an adult river otter, driven by curiosity rather than hunger, approached within a few feet of Lupa. The sleek brown mammal, with small ears, broad snout, and long tapered tail raised its head above the water and chattered excitedly at Lupa. Lupa crouched low in the water, barked nervously at his visitor, but showed no fear.

The greatest attraction of the river to the pups was not its waters but the grassy bog scattered along its low-lying banks. This was the home to hundreds of meadow voles, short-tailed shrews, and bog lemmings. All were quite odiferous and their tunnels and burrows were the targets of considerable digging by the pups. Excited sniffing and snuffing, as each youngster inhaled the fascinating scents, and frantic digging in the black muck, made the pups oblivious to their surroundings.

A yearling bobcat wandered near the rendezvous one evening when the adults were off on a hunt, but the wolf pups easily eluded its awkward pursuit. Being only slightly larger than the pups, the 20-pound bobcat had little chance of capturing one of the wolves. In a short time the bobcat abandoned his snarls and half-serious charges and wandered on upriver.

A more serious threat appeared one afternoon as the pups were playing at water's edge and the adults were taking naps on the knoll. Lupa was swimming in shallow water, in pursuit of a beaver kit that had wandered from its bank den. Silently gliding downriver came a golden eagle. The largest of aerial predators inhabiting Cheat Mountain, with a wingspan of nearly six feet, the eagle was in search of a meal. A rabbit, a groundhog, a wild turkey, a crippled deer, or a small beaver were all potential targets.

Intent on a stranded trout, Lupa was half-submerged in the chilly waters, as his awkward splashing caught the eagle's eye. With no hesitation, no sound, and no noticeable movement, the eagle slightly slanted the large primary feathers of each wing and initiated a shallow dive. When 50 feet away, the eagle folded its wings and accelerated. At a distance of ten feet, the eagle extended its death-laden feet forward. In less than a second the scimitar-sharp talons of one foot narrowly penetrated the back of the pouncing pup. The eagle attempted to fly on with its prey, but had underestimated its weight. At 20 pounds, the wildly struggling wolf pup was a heavier weight than the eagle could easily carry.

Fortunately for the pup, the eagle was a juvenile and lacked the skills necessary to kill its prey quickly. Had it been an adult the pup would have been dead. Although the eagle's talons did not puncture a vital organ, the pup was in serious trouble. If the eagle could carry the pup onto solid ground it would reposition its grip and powerful foot muscles would drive one or more talons into Lupa's heart, bringing instant death. Screaming in pain, Lupa struggled wildly and attempted to bite the flapping wings of the hungry eagle, but to no avail.

Similar to most mothers, the mother wolf slept lightly. The sound of her frightened pup immediately brought her to her feet and into a frantic race towards the river. As the eagle flailed, Verde emitted a furious growl and launched her 90-pound body from the bank. Before the talons could be repositioned, the eagle spotted Verde and released the pup. Wolf and eagle battled furiously, wings and talons against fangs. As Verde clamped her jaws onto the eagle's wing tip, the bird glimpsed Canus approaching and in an instant the large brown bird abandoned its battle and launched itself into the air. Canus bounded high off the ground, but the young eagle was already out of reach. While Verde hurried to the side of her pup the eagle followed the course of Shavers Fork on downriver with slow, powerful wing beats. A single brown primary feather floated softly to the ground, and Canus nosed it with contempt.

Lupa was the center of attention, and the blood seeping from the talon punctures elicited considerable licking by both the adults. When the bleeding ceased, his mother called Lupa to follow and led him to the safety of the red spruce stand. Lupa soon recovered from the attack and two days later had all but forgotten the near-death episode. But the subconscious memory would linger as long as he lived, improving his alertness, causing him to frequently look skyward, and ultimately increasing his odds of survival.

☙ CHAPTER SEVEN ❧
FIRST HUNT

Lupa and his siblings never ventured far from the two-acre rendezvous site until October, when a new chapter in their lives began. After lazing around the knoll the entirety of one brisk, sunny afternoon, Canus arose from his daily nap, stretched, walked a few paces towards the setting sun, pointed his nose upward in the direction of the glowing sky, and emitted the hunting howl. The pups expected a command to stay at the knoll but this October night was different. Canus and the entire pack of five adults and four pups began their first combined hunting trip. At first the pups behaved as pups, running and jumping and playing. But several painful nips from their mother convinced them this trip was serious business. In single file, with adults in the lead, yearlings following closely behind, and pups bringing up the rear, the pack headed out.

Canus planned to follow the major game trail that paralleled Shavers Fork until reaching a branch of the trail bearing west, along a small tributary. With darkness settling over Cheat Mountain the pack trotted silently through open grassy areas, under open groves of stunted maples, and through widely spaced beech trees, always following game trails. The wolves detected the distinctive scents of rabbits, red squirrels, groundhogs, and wild turkeys. But Canus was in search of larger prey. Although wolves enjoyed rabbit meat, a single rabbit would vanish in two or three swift gulps. The pack needed a larger animal.

Small elk herds were scattered throughout the region and in less than two hours of travel Canus detected the sweet smell of a nearby elk herd. Quickly ordering the pack to halt, Canus gave the hunt signal. The other adults knew exactly what to do, but the pups whined inquisitively. Instinct, however, provided them with a basic knowledge of what was expected, and the pups followed obediently as the pack spread out and crept towards the feeding elk. Stars provided enough light for the wolves to identify the elk, and each canine crouched lower to conceal its presence. The wolves were downwind of the elk, and with eyesight designed to operate at night they were better equipped than a band of Iroquois hunting in broad daylight. When the patient stalk brought the pack to within 20 yards of the elk, Canus erupted from his crouch and lunged towards the elk. The other adults immediately followed. Sensing the excitement, the pups soon entered the chase.

This hunt had followed the typical pattern: search, stalk, chase, and attack. The primary role of the alpha wolf was to identify the specific individual most vulnerable to attack. Healthy, mature individuals were ignored, in search of a youngster or a crippled adult. Wolves were aware of the dangers of hooves and antlers of adult elk, and some would bear the scars and memories for a lifetime.

Canus directed his attention towards a yearling elk that ran with an unnatural motion. By some mysterious signal, the alpha male ordered other members of the pack to target the fleeing yearling. Similar to schools of sharks or packs of killer whales, the wolves moved as a single entity close behind the elk. Cooperation was the key to the pack bringing down a much larger prey.

The chase continued for nearly 200 yards, with the wolves slowly gaining ground on the elk. A healthy yearling elk would have successfully outrun and escaped the wolf pack. But due to a malformed shoulder joint the elk was at a disadvantage. A dense mountain laurel patch slowed it perceptibly and in seconds the hunt reached its climax. Canus struck at the elk's right hind leg, severing the hamstring with the force of his sharp teeth. Another adult clamped its jaws onto the left hind leg. As the elk tumbled to the ground Verde quickly slashed the neck and cut a jugular vein. The kill was completed. In a healthy, well-balanced ecosystem no animal dies of old age.

Canus tore into a hindquarter, while Verde lapped blood from the neck. Other wolves pressed forward, but menacing growls and bared fangs warned them to stay back. One adult female came too close and received a painful bite from Canus. In less than 20 minutes the two pack leaders had each consumed ten pounds of hot elk flesh. Finally, the two satiated adults moved away from the kill, as other members of the pack, including the pups, rushed to eat. However, the pups were shouldered aside and given no opportunity to feed. For the first time in their lives no adults regurgitated piles of previously consumed meat for them. But instinct drove them to the carcass when all other members of the pack had eaten their fill. Now Lupa was the dominant individual at the kill. Much like his father, Lupa selected the choicest location, and the young male pup fed on the best remaining morsels.

Nearly 100 pounds of meat were consumed during that first feasting. With twinkling stars illuminating the scene atop Cheat Mountain, members of the pack, each featuring bloodstained faces, stretched out in tall grass to clean their fur and digest their dinner.

When the first faint sign of daylight appeared in the eastern sky, members of the pack rose, stretched, and ate again. With fewer hunger pangs and much less confrontation, the feeding party was more or less amicable. There was considerable growling, barring of teeth, and raised hackles, but no direct attacks upon the lower-ranked members. All the wolves tore off large chunks of flesh, and swallowed them whole. When all had completed their meal Canus led them on a short trek to a grassy, east-facing hillside. Here, in the warm October sunshine they spent the remaining daylight hours recovering from their "meat drunk", that state when they are barely conscious and only semi-alert. In mid-afternoon Lupa raised his head to watch a honking, V-shaped flock of Canada geese pass overhead. No geese nested in the Cheat Mountain watershed, and few ever landed during their migrations due to a lack of suitable waters.

The pack returned to the elk carcass the following night, but little flesh remained after ravens and foxes had gleaned their share. With much tugging, the wolves separated the skeleton into various pieces, and each moved off to its own feeding site. Canus claimed one hind leg, Verde the skull, and Lupa ended up with a shoulder blade. As barred owls hooted in a nearby red spruce stand, a contrasting sound of cracking bones emanated as each long bone was fractured and its marrow sucked. Ribs were crunched and the small bony pieces swallowed. With all nutrient value removed from the elk carcass and the moon high overhead, Canus again pointed his snout towards the sky and gave the hunting howl.

Canus led the pack along a well-defined game trail that continued westward, but three hours of steady travel produced no targets. Towards morning they jumped a bull elk and an hour later three white-tailed does. However, the healthy animals easily outran the pursuing wolves and the attacks were abandoned. Shortly after daylight returned to Cheat Mountain, Canus called a halt to the night's hunt and led the pack to a sunny hillside where they spent the day.

Wolves seldom ate every day, often going three days between meals. During the autumn months when most deer and elk were in superb condition, and deep snows had not yet arrived to slow their escape runs, less than 20 percent of the wolf chases were successful. Kills occurred more frequently during summer months when deer fawns and elk calves were present and again during late winter when they were in poor condition and deep snows hindered their movements.

During the late fall and early winter months Canus led his pack in a large circuitous route around the section of Cheat Mountain that was their territory. Deer and elk were abundant and the pack rarely went three nights without making a kill. Lupa gained weight rapidly and by early December weighed nearly 90 pounds. Although somewhat smaller than Canus, Lupa was larger than the yearlings and most of the adult females in both weight and girth. His size and strength enabled him to play a larger role in the hunts, and during the first week of November he made his first capture.

The pack was closing in on a young doe, which suddenly veered sharply left to avoid a dense stand of red spruce saplings. Her route took her directly into Lupa's path and with an eight-foot leap he closed the distance and clamped his jaws onto her left rear leg. His weight pulled her to the ground and in less than a minute the alpha female had clamped her jaws around the doe's throat. Lupa savagely ripped two large chunks of meat from the hindquarter before Canus drove him away. When both When both Canus and Verde had eaten their fill, Lupa claimed his feeding position. Other wolves attempted to drive him away, but Lupa growled menacingly, administered several painful bites, and refused to relinquish what he considered his rightful position. From that day on, Lupa played a major role in almost every kill. Other than Canus, no other wolf was his equal in speed, agility, and strength.

The pack typically covered nine to ten crow miles during each night's hunt, exhibiting near perpetual motion. When they had not eaten in several days, the pack would travel over 30 miles in search of game. The large feeding territory encompassed over 60 square miles. Typically, the pack would cover their entire hunting area in two or three days. They always followed existing game trails, some of which cut across the pack's territory. Canus made all required decisions regarding travel and, for reasons unknown to Lupa, would choose one route over another. All wolves faithfully followed their leader, a trait necessary in maintaining a successful pack. The Cheat Mountain pack's summer territory was approximately 6 miles wide by 12 miles long. Its eastern border was Shavers Fork River, and its western border the flanks of Cheat Mountain, including the headwaters of two small streams that would later be named Becca's (or Becky's) Creek and Riffles Creek.

The borders of the pack's territory were dotted with hundreds of scent posts, where pack members would systematically deposit their urine, thus warning other wolves they were entering a claimed territory. Scent posts typically consisted of tree trunks, but also were fallen logs, rocks, shrubs, and tufts of grass. Such posts were seldom more than 200 yards apart.

The hunting excursions of a pack around its territory were frequently interrupted as they halted to deposit a squirt of urine onto a particular post. These sites also elicited the deposition of piles of feces, to reinforce the warning to other packs. Urination and defecation were typically followed by ritualized scratching. This involved alternate motions of their right and left forelegs, synchronized with similar movements of hind legs on the opposite side. Such scratching produced a visual sign for other wolves in the pack, but also triggered the release of odors from glands in the paws.

Howling by the pack, especially following a successful kill, served to warn any wolf packs within hearing distance that they were near a claimed territory.

Although white-tailed deer were the most abundant prey available to wolves in the region, elk were the key to their food base. One deer would not satisfy the pent-up hunger of the pack. With each wolf typically consuming 10-15 pounds of meat per day, the 50-60 pounds of meat on an adult deer did not fill the stomachs of a pack of 11 wolves. An adult elk was another matter, providing at least 200 pounds of rich red meat.

Elk began their migration off the peaks of Cheat Mountain in October, as lush grasses and forbs and shrubs of summer entered dormancy. By November, deep snows made it nearly impossible for elk to secure a nutritious meal in the mountains. Many elk trekked down off the mountain to the sheltered valley positioned to the west—a basin that would eventually be called Tygart Valley. At 2,000 feet elevation, this broad, relatively flat valley was much more hospitable to elk, and to wolves, than were the surrounding mountains.

By November, buffalo had moved to the gentler climate offered by the Shenandoah Valley and only white-tailed deer and elk provided enough meat to satisfy the demands of a wolf pack. But the Cheat Mountain pack was overseen by veterans, and seldom did a week go by that they did not gorge on the warm flesh of some hoofed animal. So it was that Lupa and his pack spent the remainder of that winter in the bottomlands of Tygart Valley.

❧ CHAPTER EIGHT ❦
MATING SEASON

One day in late February, Lupa was surprised to see Canus playfully dance around Verde, while wagging his tail, nipping her ears, and rubbing his face against hers. This unusual behavior, which Lupa had never before witnessed, continued for nearly two hours. All members of the pack anxiously attempted to join in the frolic but whenever one of the other adult females approached, Canus drove her away with fierce growls and harsh bites. Courtship had begun.

For the next two weeks the daily naps and even the nightly hunts were frequently interrupted by courtship activities. With courtship came turmoil, conflict, and stress. The most serious conflicts arose between Canus and the two yearling males. These two were now sexually mature and focused almost-constant attention towards the three adult females, two of which had come into heat by the end of February. At every advance of the alpha male towards one of the adult females, the yearling males would intervene. At those times when Verde was initiating courtship by placing her forepaws and neck across Canus's shoulders one of the yearling males would attempt to squeeze between them. Canus routinely growled, snarled, and lunged at the young male. Lupa was fascinated and often attempted to join in what he thought was play.

By the first of March, Canus had mated several times with Verde and he began to focus most of his attention on the other receptive female. The larger of the yearling males, whose right ear drooped down towards his eye, attempted to mount Verde as she crouched in the snow. Canus immediately charged the yearling and delivered a deep bite to his hip. Surprised and shocked, the yearling retaliated with a bite of his own to Canus's shoulder. Blood flowed from the wounds on both wolves. The two faced off, four feet apart, with savage snarling, lips pulled back, and hair bristling on the backs. Lupa and the other wolves backed away, nervously watching the two males.

The droop-eared male suddenly charged into Canus and the two fell heavily into the snow. The combat was so intense that it was not possible to determine who was suffering the most. The snow was covered with blood, and the yearling cried in pain when Canus clamped his jaws onto a right front foot. Within seconds the droop-eared yearling was lying on his side, holding his right front foot awkwardly up in the air, while Canus stood astride him. Had the yearling rolled onto his back, signaling submission, the battle would have ended. But instead he nipped Canus on the neck. Two more savage bites were inflicted upon the yearling before the attack ended. With considerable whimpering, the yearling crawled away, then limped on three legs towards the nearby creek. Canus rushed towards him when they were 50 feet apart and inflicted another serious bite to the hindquarters.

Shortly after the battle between the two males, Canus led the pack on their nightly hunt, which ended nearly 15 miles from the injured droop-eared yearling. The yearling male spent that night and the next two days and nights lying at the edge of the tributary. The broken right front foot seriously handicapped his movements, but he was able to capture several fat meadow voles, and an immature groundhog that ventured too far from its den. The foot healed partially in the next two weeks, but was too sensitive to bear any weight. The young wolf was forced to concentrate on small rodents and his weight diminished to only 60 pounds.

The surviving yearling male demonstrated considerably less sexual activity and responded to Canus's aggressive acts by rolling onto his back and exhibiting the submissive behavior that enables members of a wolf pack to coexist. Most wolf packs consist of only one adult male, but when a second male is present he will be allowed to remain with the pack only if he exhibits submission to the alpha male. Lupa and the other ten-month old males witnessed this behavior, and subconsciously learned that their future acceptance within the pack depended upon daily submission to the alpha male.

After a gestation period of 63 days, Verde gave birth to another litter of pups. Three males and three females were born in an enlarged fox den. Verde had created two separate oval entrances, each nearly two feet in diameter. The main tunnel, which was nearly 15 feet in length, ended in the primary den where the pups were born. Several other passageways branched off the main tunnel, some leading to other entrances and some into secondary dens. Lupa was aware of the pups' presence, but never saw them until they ventured outside the den at three weeks of age. They varied in coat color from light gray to dark silver. All were lighter than Lupa, whose coat had darkened considerably following his first molt. Although Lupa was not black, he was the darkest in the pack. All six pups had blue eyes, which would not turn yellow until they reached six weeks old.

Wolf pups, similar to the young of other large predators, were typically born at a time when deer fawns and elk calves were most abundant. When wolf pups were in greatest need of meat to supplement their milk diet, fresh meat was readily available. Following the birth of her young, Verde and one or two of the females from the previous year's litter remained near the den while other members of the pack hunted.

Lupa, now one year old, accompanied the pack on all its nightly hunts. He weighed nearly 120 pounds, slightly more than Canus, and often inflicted the lethal bite when a deer or elk was brought to the ground. Following many successful hunts, Lupa returned to the den site with a stomach full of chunky deer meat. Much of this he deposited at the mouth of the den where it was consumed by Verde and the babies.

The pack's hunting behavior changed drastically during June and July, when they became a less cohesive group. Wolves began hunting alone or in pairs. Whereas the cooperation of several members of a pack was necessary to kill an adult deer or elk, a single wolf could easily kill a deer fawn or elk calf. Lupa quickly developed a search image for those newborns and spent most nights investigating areas where does and elk cows were most likely to drop their young. Dense viburnum thickets or grassy bogs were favorite birth sites, and Lupa learned to concentrate his hunting efforts in such habitats. Young rabbits and hares, plus recently hatched turkey poults and a few groundhogs also inhabited Cheat Mountain, and Lupa nightly captured two or three such prey. Because they weighed only a few pounds, several were required to satisfy his hunger. But because they were so easily captured, his efforts were amply rewarded.

It was during this period that one of the adult females and the submissive adult male separated from the pack. The two had begun hunting together in late June, and often spent lengthy periods away from the pack and the den site. By July they had moved nearly 20 miles to the east, well into the Greenbrier River drainage. There they discovered a small area not defended by another wolf pack and began scent marking the territory as their own. Summer was the ideal time to establish a new territory because food was abundant and the instinct for well-defined, established packs to defend their territories was weak.

Numerous rivers drained these highlands flowing slowly between elongated, parallel ridges that would eventually be assigned names such as North Fork Mountain, Back Allegheny Mountain, and Middle Mountain. But all streams did not flow in the same direction. Shavers Fork River flowed generally north-northeast. In marked contrast, the stream situated only two miles to the east (later named the West Fork of the Greenbrier), flowed south-southwest. Uneven uplifting and folding of the limestone and sandstone layers resulted in parallel streams flowing in opposite directions.

Individual raindrops falling from a cloud over Cheat Mountain were destined for contrasting journeys. Those falling on opposite sides of the main ridgeline separating the Shavers Fork drainage from the Greenbrier drainage would begin their long journeys in opposite directions, but would eventually join many years and hundreds of miles later where the Kanawha River joined the Ohio River.

Rainwater entering the Shavers Fork River flowed into the main branch of the Cheat River, then into the Monongahela River where it later merged with the Allegheny River to form the Ohio. At that point it turns south and toward the Gulf of Mexico.

Waters falling into the West Fork of the Greenbrier eventually joined waters of the Kanawha River and subsequently merged with waters of the Ohio at Point Pleasant, West Virginia. Waters from the Shavers Fork River would travel about 525 miles to reach Pt. Pleasant on the Ohio River, by way of Pittsburgh, Pennsylvania. Waters from the West Fork of the Greenbrier would travel about 340 miles before reaching Point Pleasant.

EDWIN DARYL MICHAEL

❦ *CHAPTER NINE* ❧
OTHER PREDATORS

Lupa began to hunt alone during July, honing the techniques necessary to bring down a deer or elk. Like most wolves of the pack, Lupa returned to the den site at the end of a night's hunt. The adults of the pack, and the yearling littermates, spent the long summer days near the den, typically sleeping, while the pups pestered those who were closest to the mouth of the den. In August, when the pups were five months old, Verde moved them to a rendezvous site nearly five miles upstream. The lightly wooded knoll overlooked the Shavers Fork and provided an excellent site for the pups to complete their summer's development. Dense stands of viburnum and rhododendron provided cover where they could escape detection if larger predators should wander past. The thickets also obscured them from any golden eagles that might be flying overhead.

As dusk settled over the mountains, flying squirrels, woodrats, and other nocturnal rodents began their own food searches. Members of the pack would simultaneously depart on their nightly hunts. Some hunted alone, others hunted in pairs, and a few ventured into the night as a small pack.

This late summer hunting routine continued until early October, when the pack regrouped as one unit and all members, including the pups, ventured out in their nightly hunting forays. With Canus leading, followed closely by Lupa, the pack traversed first one game trail and then another until a likely target was detected. Full-grown, healthy elk and mature white-tailed bucks were not pursued more than 50 yards before the alpha male determined the chance of success and the risk of injury were too great. Even adult white-tailed deer does and yearling elk were typically not chased more than a few hundred yards. Only when the alpha male judged the animal to be vulnerable to attack did he initiate a serious chase.

Timber wolves were not the only large predators atop Cheat Mountain. Cougars (called mountain lions by some and panthers by others) and black bears were the largest. Cougars were approximately the same weight as timber wolves, while black bears were considerably heavier—reaching 600 pounds. Mid-size predators included the bobcat, fisher, and gray fox. Golden eagles were the only avian predator of any size.

Only the cougar was in direct competition with timber wolves for food throughout the year, both predators of the same prey. Although their hunting techniques differed drastically, the results were the same—a dead deer or elk. Wolves hunted in packs, running in pursuit of their prey until close enough to make the kill. Cougars hunted alone, waiting patiently at a strategic site where they could leap upon the unsuspecting prey.

Black bears rarely killed adult deer or elk, although they voraciously consumed any carrion they discovered. Bears were omnivores as well as scavengers. Berries, fruits, ants, fish, grasses, acorns, and beechnuts, plus newborn deer fawns and elk calves were their favorites. Because they hibernated throughout the harsh winter months they did not compete directly with wolves when deep snows made the hoofed prey more vulnerable.

Fisher, foxes, and bobcats were much more numerous than wolves, but were not capable of killing adult deer or elk, and only occasionally killed a newborn deer fawn or elk calf. They typically hunted small prey, such as rabbits, hares, groundhogs, grouse, wild turkey, and mice. Although such small prey would have provided a gratifying meal to timber wolves, the pounds of meat obtained from such a small animal did not justify the time and energy expended, especially in winter months when burrowing and flight improved escape. Also, if wolves concentrated on rodents they would be competing directly with the mid-sized predators, animals much better adapted to capturing small prey than wolves. Specialization among predators had resulted in wolves concentrating on hoofed mammals.

The pack encountered various predators on a daily basis. The encounters typically were uneventful, with no altercations, but this was not always the case.

Late in September, as the wolves were coursing slowly along a game trail through a blueberry thicket atop Cheat Mountain they detected the scent of black bear. Several frosts and one hard freeze had occurred that autumn, and the open area was ablaze in color. One small isolated stand of quaking aspen emitted a golden glow from its constantly shimmering circular leaves. Stunted maples were highlighted by foliage of various shades of red. The beech trees contributed browns while deep greens emanated from the stands of spruce. Reddish-orange clusters of mountain ash berries gave the appearance of ornaments upon the ten-foot tall trees. Most striking were the large expanses of glorious crimson created by the frosted blueberry leaves.

Canus slowed his pace of travel and nearly halted as the pack topped a small knoll. Three hundred yards upwind of them was an adult black bear and her two cubs, each weighing about 80 pounds. The three bears were roaming through the blueberry thicket, searching for the last of the year's crop. They raked in handfuls of berries, as well as compliments of leaves. Being omnivores, the bears would receive nutritional value from both the leaves and the berries.

Canus and Verde harbored a deep hatred towards all black bears. Seasons past, when they had functioned as a two-wolf pack, a large male black bear dug out and killed all four of their young pups. Typically, one adult remained at the den in case danger should threaten. However, when the pups neared whelping stage the parents hunted together to satisfy the ever-growing needs of their family. On that one particular night the male and female had returned from their hunt as the bear was eating the fourth pup. The wolves managed to drive away the bruin but halted their pursuit to search for the pups. For nearly one week the female wolf remained at the destroyed den site while the male hunted alone, bringing back food to sustain her during that period. The pair abandoned the den site and spent the next 11 months wandering throughout their territory.

Now years later, the pack silently studied the scene before them. After nearly five minutes Canus emitted several low yips and whines. By communication perfected through wolf evolution, the male transmitted directions to his pack. Quietly, the pack divided and two groups moved in opposite directions while the alpha male remained stationary. When separated by 100 yards, Canus issued the command to move forward and the two groups began to flank the bears. As they reached points opposite their target, Canus began his charge.

The mother bear became aware of the charging wolves when they were less than 40 yards away, and she immediately bounded through the blueberry stand in search of safety. One cub followed close behind, but the second cub headed for a stand of red spruce at the edge of a small bog. With claws digging deeply in the bark of a spruce tree, the cub began its climb to safety. Lupa had outrun all other wolves and leaped for the cub as its front paws grasped the lowest limb. With a powerful clamp of jaws the weight of the wolf pulled the cub to the ground. The alpha wolf and one adult female immediately charged into the fray and life ended quickly for the cub. Canus sat on his haunches, raised his head to the sky, and sent a victory howl across the blueberry flat. Other members of the pack joined and in less than 30 minutes only the shattered skeleton of the cub remained.

The wolves set off in pursuit of the mother bear and her other cub but they had reached the safety of a large hemlock and from their lofty perch had little to fear from the wolves. Venting their hatred of the bears, the wolves circled beneath them, while barking and howling.

With their appetite only slightly whetted, the wolves continued their nightly hunting foray and two hours later Canus initiated the stalk of a yearling whitetailed doe. The chase and then the attack were successful and in the morning the wolves stretched out lazily on a nearby hilltop.

The wolves returned to the deer carcass late the next afternoon and surprised a gray fox that was focused intently on gleaning the remaining bits of flesh and fat. The fox jerked his snout from inside the pelvic girdle and frantically sprinted away. Other pack members focused on the deer carcass, but Lupa erupted in pursuit of the fox. Before it had covered twenty yards Lupa clamped his jaws onto its back. The fox was killed instantly and Lupa hungrily tore three large chunks of flesh from the hind legs. In less than fifteen minutes the young wolf consumed the entire fox, other than its head, tail, and innards. An eight-pound fox provides little nourishment for a hungry wolf.

Meanwhile, Canus had claimed one of the large thighbones and managed to crack it with his powerful jaws and bone-crushing molars. Other wolves were soon cracking leg bones and rib bones from the deer carcass. The marrow provided a special treat.

Another encounter with a large predator occurred one cold night in November. The pack surprised a young mountain lion as it fed on a white-tailed deer yearling. The cat was a juvenile male, almost two years old, but not fully-grown nor fully experienced in being on its own. Its mother had forced it away as she entered another breeding cycle, and a courting male cougar had provided the final excuse for the juvenile to begin its solitary life.

The young cougar courageously defended the deer carcass, with snarls, ears laid back, glaring yellow eyes, bared canine teeth, and ferocious clawing lunges towards any wolf that came within five yards. A storm the previous day had dumped nearly two feet of snow on the mountains, and a half moon created a well-illuminated scene. The silent wolf pack encircled the big cat, slowly tightening the circle. Constant feints towards the cat were well coordinated, with those wolves situated at the cat's rear charging ever closer when the cat itself lunged at the nearest wolf. The cat was forced into almost constant action as it whirled rapidly to face those attacking from its rear.

Lupa was the first to make physical contact with the cougar, and his bold move was nearly fatal. As the cat whirled to face a wolf positioned opposite Lupa, the feline's three-foot long tail swept through the air and landed within two feet of Lupa. He instinctively lunged at the tail and gripped its tip. As Lupa's front incisors tightly pinched the tail, the cat reacted instantly. Whirling around, it jerked its tail from Lupa's mouth and threw a potentially fatal strike at Lupa. Saber sharp claws raked Lupa's shoulder, but did not penetrate deeply. Lupa sprung backward escaping a second swipe by the cat.

The courageous cougar temporarily ceased its lunges and crouched close to the ground, but there was no cessation to its snarling. Gaining confidence, the wolves inched ever closer until several were within ten feet. At that point, the young cougar launched itself high over the nearest wolf and hit the ground running. Wind-driven snow stung his eyes and blurred his vision. Lupa and two yearlings ran wildly after the cat, but were unable to gain ground during the chase. In less than 200 yards, the cat reached a large pile of boulders and backed into a small cave. From that strategic position the wolves had no chance of inflicting injury on the cat or forcing it to flee.

While the three young wolves had recklessly pursued the cat, the adult wolves began their own attack. This one focused on the deer carcass. By the time Lupa and the other young wolves abandoned their pursuit, the adult wolves had completed their meal.

❧ CHAPTER TEN ❦
THE FIRST SETTLERS

During the late 1750s and early 1760s, timber wolves of Cheat Mountain witnessed from afar the first appearances of Europeans. Explorers and fur traders, with names such as Christopher Gist, Colonel Croghan, Thomas Cresap, and Samuel Eckerlin, explored the area. Most departed from Philadelphia and Lancaster, traversed the mountains of central Pennsylvania, then crossed through western Pennsylvania to the banks of the Monongahela River. Others followed the North Branch of the Potomac River to Wills Creek, Maryland (later to be named Cumberland), then crossed Chestnut Ridge before reaching the banks of the Monongahela. From there they traveled upstream (southward) to reach the broad fertile valleys that supported herds of deer, elk, and bison, and the numerous tributaries full of valuable furbearers.

Other explorers and trappers followed the South Branch of the Potomac River through Virginia and crossed the Allegheny Front at the few passes and gaps where Indian trails avoided the steepest and highest crags. One such route departed the South Branch Valley near Seneca Rocks, turned west, and followed waterways that would someday be named Seneca Creek, Whites Run, and the Dry Fork River, a major tributary of the Cheat River. From there travelers could follow other drainages and mountain passes and move even deeper into the rugged Appalachians.

Such routes followed previously established trails, which had in turn traced centuries-old buffalo trails. Major routes passing into the central Appalachians included the Shawnee Trail/Seneca Trail, and the North Fork/Shavers Fork Trail.

Whereas travel to the South Branch Valley and the Monongahela Valley was relatively easy, travel up and over the central Appalachians, especially that segment labeled the Allegheny Front, was so daunting it was rarely attempted. Travel on horseback was possible, if the major Indian trails were followed, but it was impossible to move wagons up and over the Allegheny Front. Cliffs, crags, boulder-dominated ridges, twisted outcrops, and steep ravines created a long linear barrier sufficient to stop most westward travel. Add the synergistic effect of "laurel" thickets (primarily rhododendron) and red spruce stands, and neither man nor beast was eager to attempt penetration into the depths of this great wilderness.

The original Appalachian Mountains were the highest mountains in North America, much higher than the current Rocky Mountains, which climb over 14,000 feet into the clouds. Freezing, thawing, winds, and torrential rains gradually eroded away the peaks of the Appalachians. Great loads of rocky material were carried ever so slowly towards the streams and rivers that cut through the mountains. Rock, gravel, and sand slowly accumulated at the lowest elevations. Broad, relatively flat valley floors were created, providing fertile beds for a variety of plants. No glaciers ever scoured the mountains or gouged out the valleys along Cheat Mountain, although numerous snow packs within boulder fields persisted long into summer months. The nearest glaciers had remained nearly 150 miles north of Cheat Mountain, in what is now central Pennsylvania. Despite that fact, the imperceptibly slow erosion of the peaks had resulted in a region characterized by densely packed ridges and peaks.

Winter storms arrived early on Cheat Mountain in 1753 and Canus and his pack followed the elk herds off the mountain to the great valley lying to the west. With a width of over two miles and a length of nearly 30, these flatlands were at an elevation around 2,000 feet. This bottomland was low enough below the adjacent mountains, which reached 4,000 feet, to provide relatively mild winters for wildlife that neither migrated nor hibernated. Throughout October, the wolf pack daily traversed the foothills that skirted Cheat Mountain. Here they intercepted elk that were pushed out of the higher elevations by deep snowdrifts. Almost daily the pack killed an elk or a deer, and strengthened their muscles and built up the fat layers essential to survival through the upcoming winter.

One crisp night, with a blanket of new-fallen snow illuminating the landscape, the pack trotted along the banks of a large stream. A vagrant gust of wind swept through the hemlocks, cascading a small cloud of snow onto Lupa's head. Canus was the first to detect a fascinating odor, and immediately swung his pack towards the source. All wolves soon became aware of the strange odor, and excitement coursed through the pack. The odor was much stronger than that of a single elk or deer, although very similar in nature. In less than 20 minutes the pack detected splashing in the stream, and their trotting changed to a ground-covering, fast lope. Suddenly into view came nine large, bulky buffalo. They were crossing the stream, and the mature cow that led the small herd was climbing the stream bank on the opposite side, while the other eight were splashing through the shallows at the crossing.

Lupa pushed closer to Canus and was close on his heels when Canus vaulted off the stream bank in pursuit. With three mighty leaps the wolves were alongside the young female buffalo that brought up the rear. It was a six-month old calf, but weighed as much as a yearling bull elk. Undaunted by its bulk, Lupa sprung at the buffalo, aiming for its left hind leg. However, the stream was chest-deep on the wolves, and splashing water limited their vision. Lupa hit high on the buffalo's flank, at the point where the thighbone joined the hip socket, and his teeth failed to clamp solidly. With near constant bellowing, the buffalo herd exploded up over the bank.

The wolves were accustomed to failed attacks, typically experiencing success only once in ten tries. This time though Canus did not signal his pack to abandon the chase. While the buffalo galloped up the sloping hillside the wolf pack rapidly drew closer. Four wolves leaped but the buffalo were more difficult to bring down than even the largest bull elk. After a chase of 200 yards, the buffalo stopped and formed a tight circle. The wolves halted their attacks and encircled their prey. Most wolves sat on their haunches, while others feinted charges towards the stomping buffalo.

Lupa made one more ill advised leap, but was met by the bony head of a young bull. The bull's horn slashed a shallow groove across Lupa's shoulder, and the wolf sprung to safety after falling to the snow-covered ground. As blood dripped onto the snow, Lupa crouched close to the ground and studied the prey. They were quite stocky in build, with a massive bulky head, a high hump on their shoulders, and short legs. They were one of the few hoofed mammals in the world whose forequarters were more massive than their hindquarters. Long shaggy hair covered much of the front half of each buffalo. A full-grown buffalo weighed about 2,000 pounds, compared to an adult bull elk, which often weighed 1,000 pounds, and white-tailed deer bucks, which could reach 300 pounds.

This herd had experienced numerous wolf attacks throughout their existence, and had never lost a member of the herd to a wolf. Having learned they were vulnerable to attack only when running, the lead cow urged the remainder of the herd to remain in a tight cluster. After 30 minutes, Canus rose and led the wolf pack away. Other than a few shallow cuts, neither buffalo nor wolf had suffered any injuries. As if convinced by the wolf attack that it was time to head for greener pastures, the buffalo herd departed the valley the following day. They would spend the winter in the Shenandoah Valley and return the following summer to the Cheat Mountains.

In early November, Canus led his pack out of the foothills and reestablished their territory throughout the floor of the broad valley. The pack circled the southern end of their territory, scent marking its perimeter to warn a neighbor pack to avoid that specific locale. Their territory was situated on both sides of the small, meandering river on the valley floor. By November, much of the river was ice-covered, allowing easy crossing by the wolves.

Later in November, Canus led his pack into the northern stretches of their territory. One morning, while resting from the nighttime hunt, sensitive wolf noses detected the alien odor that wrought much fear—smoke. Unbeknownst to the wolves, the northern end of the valley had been invaded by a new entity the previous spring. Whereas no Indian villages had ever existed in the valley, it now supported two white families. Robert Files and David Tygart had moved their families into the area the previous spring soon after the snows melted. They felled hundreds of trees to create openings in the dense bottomland forest where crops could be grown, using the resultant logs for cabins, barns, and outhouses. Other trees were girdled and remained standing as silent sentinels over the cropland. With no tree leaves to block the sun's rays, the earth warmed and sunlight triggered growth in the small bean, corn, and squash seedlings that emerged.

The Files' and Tygart's cabins were about two miles apart, and smoke swirled out of both stone chimneys that November day in 1753 when Lupa and the pack made their disturbing discovery. Canus led his pack in a circuit around the cabin of Robert Files, but stopped on a high knoll to identify the source of the smoke. While sitting on one such knoll, Lupa detected two men splitting logs. Their scent drifted past the knoll and Lupa expanded his store of knowledge to include human odor.

During that autumn the wolves encountered human scent on several occasions, and discretely studied the men as they hunted to feed their own families. Canus avoided the immediate area around the cabins, with its ever-present odors of wood smoke and humans. Fortunately for everyone concerned, the wolves never attacked the horses and cattle the settlers had brought over the mountains—possibly due to an abundance of native hoofed prey.

By mid-December, the wolf pack again ventured into the northern reaches of their winter range. Although downwind of the Files' cabin, they detected no smoke, but instead noted the odor of death. Such scent usually meant the carcass of a dead animal and possible food. Thus, Canus led his pack on a close investigation. They did find a carcass, but not that of a wild animal. It was the remains of Robert Files.

Lupa closely approached the remains, and after licking at the exposed face prepared to bite the exposed neck. However, a fierce growl from the alpha male warned him to move away from the settler's remains. After a few moments of nervous investigation of the scene, Canus directed his pack away from the cabin.

Indians had killed Robert, his wife, and five children. One son, who was working alone on a nearby hillside, had witnessed the attack and fled to the David Tygart house where he warned them of the danger. David urgently gathered all his family into the log cabin, piled firewood in front of the main door, and equipped them with whatever weapons were available. Those without rifles were given knives, axes, and sickles. The Indians did not attack the Tygart cabin, and continued their trek northward to their winter settlement in New York.

The Tygarts discovered the bodies of Robert Files and his family the following day but were unable to bury them due to the frozen ground, as well as fear of the Indians' return. David Tygart quickly made the painful decision to depart the valley, and Cheat Mountain was once again void of white settlers. The alpha wolf intentionally led his pack around the Files' and Tygart's cabins throughout their hunting excursions that winter, and Lupa sensed that humans and their cabins were to be avoided. The Indians in the central Appalachians harbored growing hostility towards white men, and it would be another 18 years before the lure of fertile valley soils drew another white family into the region.

᧞ CHAPTER ELEVEN ᧟
NEW ALPHA MALE

The spring of 1754 was a milestone for the pack. Serious conflict first arose when Canus began his annual courtship of the alpha female. Lupa was now sexually mature and was attracted to the alpha female. Although younger and less experienced than Canus, Lupa was considerably larger. As Verde and then another mature female showed signs of heat, conflicts between the adult males became common. At first Lupa retreated before Canus, but as the youngster's hormones surged he became more and more aggressive.

Finally the issue came to a climax. One mid-March day, as Canus attempted to mount Verde, Lupa charged fiercely and inflicted a major bite on his shoulder. In the combat that followed, Lupa tore Canus' left ear nearly off, sunk his canines into his neck, and succeeded in knocking him off his feet. Never had Canus faced such an aggressive, determined opponent. Canus fought fiercely, but was decisively outmatched. Lupa was nearly three years old and in the prime of life, whereas Canus was entering old age at 13 years.

The contest ended with blood on the snow and Canus tucking his tail between his legs, arching his back, and slinking off into a nearby spruce stand in defeat. Lupa pursued aggressively, inflicting several more bites to the alpha male's rump before returning to Verde, claiming her for his own.

That summer of 1754 the wildlife on Cheat Mountain was unchanged from previous years. The wolf pack hunted nightly, a litter of pups was born in late May, a rendezvous site was later selected, and life and death continued as it had for hundreds of years. Lupa became one of the most successful leaders the pack had ever experienced. He had an extraordinary instinct for selecting which trail to follow and which prey to target. Because of his large size he became more aggressive attacking large prey than Canus had. Hundreds of large deer and elk, including healthy mature animals, were brought to the ground as a result of his size and skills. As a result, his pack seldom went more than two days without eating and pack members grew strong.

Many birds shared the Cheat Mountains with the wolf pack each summer. By May most avian migrants had returned from their winter stay in warmer climes of Mexico and Central America. Especially evident, by sound if not by sight, were the warblers, whose dawn chorus announced the beginnings of a new day. Lupa was aware of these songs and calls, but because the birds were not a part of the pack's diet they were largely ignored. The drumming of ruffed grouse and the mating gobbles of wild turkey garnered the wolf's attention, but not as potential food to be pursued. Frequency and consistency of the two sounds informed Lupa that all was serene in the forest, and the wolf pack need not fear intruders. Male grouse typically strutted and drummed from atop a downed log but because they became hyper alert during the mating season it was nearly impossible for a wolf, or any other ground predator, to stalk close enough to make a kill.

Wild turkeys were performing at the same time, with strutting gobblers choosing open patches in the forest, which provided a broad view of the surroundings. Had a mountain lion or another larger predator, man or beast, been detected by a strutting turkey, his gobbling would have immediately ceased. By late June, the avian chorus had entered the silence phase. Mating had been completed, and eggs were being incubated or young were being fed. Calls and songs at this stage would not benefit the birds, but instead would attract predators to the vulnerable young.

One group of birds did interest of the pack. These were the passenger pigeons. For several years one particular flock had returned to the Cheat Mountains to roost. The specific forest stand chosen as the "nesting" was dominated by a dense mixture of chestnut trees and hemlocks. Passenger pigeons were a social species that required a dense concentration for the breeding cycle to be a success. The flock nesting on Cheat Mountain numbered over 800,000 and resulted in 400,000 nests being constructed. Individual trees often housed more than 1,000 nests. The small nest created by each pair of pigeons was quite flimsy in nature, with a few small twigs and sticks being lodged into the forks of a limb. Although not woven into a bowl like most bird nests, they nevertheless prevented the single egg, found in most nests, from falling through.

However, eggs and even hatchlings did occasionally fall through the nest, and as the squabs grew larger and began exercising their wings, many accidentally fell. Lupa led his pack through the nesting at least one night each week, usually prior to the initiation of their evening hunt. The fallen eggs and squabs served as tasty appetizers. However, each visit was hurried because of the great amounts of pigeon droppings raining onto their heads.

Despite the near limitless numbers of passenger pigeons, the bird of greatest importance to the wolf pack was the raven. As permanent year-round residents, wolves and ravens were involved in what might be termed a commensal relationship, one in which each species benefits from the presence of the other. Ravens were omnivores, eating a mixture of plants and animals. In summer they fed on a wide variety of foods. But in winter, they fed almost exclusively on animal matter. Not equipped to kill their prey, they depended on finding the carcasses of dead deer and elk. Ravens frequently shadowed the movements of a wolf pack as they hunted during the winter months. After making a kill, and eating their fill, the wolves would abandon the carcass and sleep for six to eight hours. During that time, ravens would boldly glean bits of fat and flesh from the bones.

On other occasions these cousins of crows, with their unique croaks, would themselves lead the wolf pack to the carcass of a winter-killed deer or elk—not intentionally, but incidentally. Ravens, typically solitary birds, spent much of the daylight hours soaring high over the mountains and valleys, and thus detected many carcasses that would have gone unnoticed by the wolf pack. Upon spotting a potential meal, a solitary raven would circle several times to analyze the situation, and then dive down for a closer examination.

Each soaring raven spent an equal amount of time searching for carcasses on the ground and observing other ravens circling in the sky. Those ravens within 1-2 miles would detect the revealing flight behavior and quickly join. Within 10-15 minutes of the original raven spotting a carcass, as many as 15 ravens would be concentrated around the find. Thus an unparalleled informal cooperation assured every raven that it could share equally in any carcass found by other ravens.

A pack of hunting wolves was equally aware of the significance of circling ravens and their downward dives. On more than one occasion, Lupa focused his attention on a group of circling-diving ravens and led his pack to the site. Typically, the wolves drove off the ravens, which could only scold in frustration.

Ravens did not intentionally emit a signal to attract other ravens, and certainly not to attract wolves. However, their survival during the long, cold, Appalachian winter was dependent on this manner of cooperation. A lone raven had a much poorer chance of finding food in winter than did 10-20 birds searching independently over separate portions of the mountain. The success of this hunting strategy by the ravens was dependent not on croaking vocalizations, but on visibility from long distances. Their black, glossy coloration enabled this. No other color could so effectively reveal the presence and behavior of a bird, whether in the sky or on the ground, whether against a backdrop of green leaves or brown grass, gray rocks or white snow. Whether the sky was bright blue, pale white, or dark ominous gray, no color was more visible than black, and the blacker the better. And ravens are black from bill to tail, unlike the mottled blend of most birds' plumage. Whether seen from above or below, whether from in front or behind, they are solid glossy black.

The value of black plumage holds true not only for ravens, but also for crows and vultures. Both are adorned with coal-black feathers. And both crows and vultures benefit from being able to monitor the behavior of other individuals from long distances. Turkey vultures spent the summer months scattered throughout the mountains and valleys, but most typically migrated out of the mountains during the cold, snowy months. Thus, they rarely "shared" the carcasses of deer and elk with ravens or wolves during winter.

In summer, vultures were usually the first to detect a dead or dying animal, due to their acute olfactory sense, superb eyesight, and the fact that they devoted the majority of daylight hours to soaring high above the earth scouring the terrain. One circling or diving vulture attracted others, which in turn attracted ravens and crows. A dead elk typically was surrounded by several dozen of the black scavengers, accompanied by much strife and conflict. Unfortunately, the birds were unable to open the carcass of an adult buffalo, elk, or deer. They could feast on the eyeballs and tongue, but their beaks were unable to penetrate the tough hide of a large mammal. Only bears, mountain lions, and wolves could accomplish that feat.

Once the wolf pack had consumed all their stomachs could hold, they typically abandoned the carcass and moved to a knoll where they slept for several hours. If the wolves departed during daylight hours, ravens and vultures moved in to fight over the remaining scraps. When their hunger had been satiated, little remained on the bones. If the wolves departed after dark, foxes, bobcats, and weasels appeared. Shrews and mice would later visit the carcass, as would woodpeckers, blue jays, and chickadees. Each gleaned whatever scraps of flesh or fat remained on the hide or bones. Top predators, those atop a food chain, have a direct impact on the community scavengers—the greater the number of wolves, the greater the number of scavengers.

EDWIN DARYL MICHAEL

❧ *CHAPTER TWELVE* ❧
DEATH OF A LEADER

Lupa led his followers through ten years of struggles involving forest fires, deep snows, food shortages, swollen rivers, other wolf packs, and encounters with numerous large predators. In every situation, the pack survived, although on rare occasions an individual wolf would lose its life.

The winter of 1764-65 was especially challenging. The near constant extreme cold resulted in snow five feet in many places. Wolves were handicapped by the deep snows, but less so than were the hoofed animals. In some areas wolves could run on the crust that had formed atop the snow, giving them a great advantage over the hoofed animals, whose small sharp hooves sunk deeply at every tiring step. When the snow crust was substantial, wolves feasted on fresh elk and deer meat. But when there was no crust and the elk sunk chest deep, wolves were required to plunge wildly to keep their heads above the snowdrifts. Such efforts tired the wolves in less than 20 yards and chases more often than not ended in failure. Fortunately for the wolves, by February the deep snows, extreme cold, and lack of forage produced one or more dead deer every night. Such starved deer had little body fat, but still satisfied the minimal needs of the wolf pack.

By March, snow depths had decreased to less than three feet deep, with most surfaces crusty enough to support the wolves. However, along the slopes leading to the higher elevations, deep drifts persisted into April. With the urge to begin their annual migration into the high mountain meadows growing stronger every day, the elk herd pushed boldly through the deep snows.

Lupa arose from his afternoon bed overlooking the headwaters of Riffles Creek and quietly announced that they should begin preparation for their nightly hunt. The pack had not made a kill in three days and sorely needed an elk or deer. The wolves were in their worst physical condition of the past nine months. Each had lost over ten pounds, and muscles were growing weak.

Nighttime hunts were the norm, with daytimes usually spent sleeping and resting. The darkness of night enabled the wolves to stalk closer to their prey than would have been possible during daylight hours, primarily because a wolf's sense of smell surpassed that of its prey. In addition, it was easier to stay warm at night when moving and easier to sleep during daytime in a warming sun.

Shortly before midnight, the pack detected a sound they had not heard in nearly six months—the quiet lowing and bellowing of buffalo. One small herd was making its annual return to the fertile grasses of Tygart Valley where in two months reddish brown calves would be born. Emitting the howl that announced a hunt, Lupa excitedly led his pack downwind of the herd of buffalo. At 40 yards out, Lupa crouched and directed the members of the pack to spread out in preparation for the final stalk. While struggling through snowdrifts beneath a hemlock stand, Lupa crept to within 20 yards of the buffalo.

Emitting a signal undetectable by the buffalo, Lupa commanded the charge to begin. Silently, the entire pack spurted through the hemlocks and into the deep snowdrift where the buffalo were standing. All of the large hoofed animals in the herd exceeded 500 pounds and no easy targets were obvious to Lupa. As the buffalo formed a compact group, with tails nearly touching and massive heads facing outward, the wolves closed to within ten yards. Amidst much bawling and snorting, the pack charged in for the kill. Lupa focused his efforts on a 10-month old yearling, and charged fearlessly at its shoulder. Several other pack members followed his lead, and in no time five other wolves were leaping into the fray. As usual, Lupa made the boldest moves—moves that would typically have targeted the prey's hindquarters rather than its head.

Normally the pack would have abandoned the attacks when a kill did not result and when it was obvious the prey posed a definite threat to the safety of the wolves. This night though, hunger, and the pressure of being pack leader, resulted in persistent attacks by Lupa. Nearly 30 minutes passed and no buffalo had experienced a serious injury. With lips curled back, the hair on his back stiffly erected, ears laid back, and eyes glaring wildly, Lupa sprang for the exposed muzzle of the yearling. This was one of his favorite holds, one typically leading to the death of the prey. When his powerful jaws clamped around the buffalo's muzzle, Lupa expected the buffalo to lose its balance and fall onto its side because elk typically did so. However, the alpha wolf was jerked violently sideways when the buffalo swung its head from side to side. Had the buffalo been alone, the other wolves would have attacked its hindquarters and the animal would have been quickly knocked off its feet. The buffalo, however, was much too powerful and maintained its firm footing in the snowdrift. As blood spilled from its muzzle, the buffalo gave a violent swing of its head. In so doing, Lupa was incidentally struck by the horn of a mature cow standing nearby. Although the cow's horn was less than half the size of that of the lead bull, it was long enough to plunge deeply into Lupa's ribcage. The wolf kept his jaws locked for another 30 seconds, but as blood pumped out of his wound, he relinquished his hold and dropped awkwardly onto the snow.

Under a waning moon, the pack members continued their short, bluffing charges for a few minutes but when they became aware of their leader lying still in the snow they backed off and sat silently on their haunches. The buffalo held their bunched formation for 20 more minutes, and then began backing away from the now motionless wolf covered in blood. The life of Lupa had come to an end.

As a bank of clouds spread deeper and darkness settled over the mountain, the buffalo slowly moved down the slope towards the bottomlands where they would spend the summer. Meanwhile, the wolf pack milled aimlessly around its fallen pack leader. A few young wolves began eating the bloody snow around Lupa and then one licked the blood still oozing from the gory wound. Starvation and the desire to survive overpowered the fear and respect the young wolves had previously held for Lupa. The largest of the juvenile males clamped his jaws on the loose hide surrounding the puncture wound and the other juvenile male grabbed savagely for his share. Amidst much snarling and shoving and snapping the body of the former leader was quickly reduced to a mangled head, several scattered bones, a few clumps of bloody hide, and a scruffy tail.

April was a difficult time for the surviving members of the pack. Hunts were much less successful with no alpha male to lead them. The alpha female assumed the duties formerly held by her mate and the pack made enough kills and located enough carcasses of winter-starved animals to prevent starvation. By May, bare ground dominated the slopes and upper plateaus, and only a few scattered drifts survived the warm rains. Litters of beaver and groundhogs were exploring outside their dens, while turkey poults ranged through the grassy openings in search of insects as sun-warmed spruce needles produced a spicy odor. By June, white-tailed does were dropping their fawns and elk cows were dropping their calves. Prey once again became plentiful and rarely would a wolf go more than one day without eating.

The adult males of the pack engaged in near-endless conflicts, some psychological but others physically violent. Eventually, it became obvious to all involved that "Blancus", a powerful two-year-old male, possessed the traits and skills necessary to be the pack's leader. Until his untimely death nearly 11 years later, he would lead the pack. Although Lupa would never again lead the pack on its nighttime hunts or bring down a white-tailed deer, his genes still flowed through the new pack that now formed. He had sired Blancus, as well as most of the other wolves now forming the pack.

❧ *CHAPTER THIRTEEN* ❧
HUNTERS AND MUZZLELOADERS

The 1770s brought an end to life as previously experienced by the pack and by most other plants and animals of the region. Historically, wolf packs, elk herds, passenger pigeon flocks, beaver colonies, chestnut forests, red spruce stands, and myriad other entities had interacted smoothly—each an integral component of the wilderness ecosystem. Certainly, extreme weather patterns resulted in populations fluctuating up and down, but in general the overall ecosystem was relatively stable. But this long period of stability was rapidly coming to an unfortunate end.

Beginning in 1772, large numbers of white families began to settle Tygart Valley and its immediate surroundings. While the word "settle" has gained widespread use to mean the establishment of farms and concentrations of houses, a more descriptive word would have been "disrupt." White families from the east coast certainly did not "settle" (as to calm) Tygart Valley or the myriad other areas where they cleared forests and erected cabins and barns. For the wildlife and forests, streams and soils, disturbance and destruction were to become daily occurrences. Life would never be the same for Tygart Valley and its wildlife communities.

Families named Conley, Crouch, Haddan, Nelson, Stalnaker, Riffle, Wamsley, Whitman, and Warwick moved into Tygart Valley and numerous, widely-scattered clearings appeared within the dense hardwood forest shortly after. During the 1772-1774 period the forest clearings gradually expanded from a few acres each to hundreds of acres. Mature trees of ash, oak, poplar, and white pine were hurriedly converted into rough but sturdy log cabins, barns, chicken houses, smokehouses, and outhouses. Pastureland, cornfields, and wheat fields replaced forests in the fertile bottomlands adjacent to the river that flowed slowly through the valley—a river that would eventually be known as Tygart Valley River, or the Tygart River, or simply the Tygart.

Typical of the many families who chose to settle the valley were the Haddan brothers: John, David, and William. The trio built their homesteads near where the town of Huttonsville would eventually be established, slightly downstream of where Riffles Creek and Becky's Creek joined with the larger waters of the Tygart River.

The favored winter hunting grounds of the wolf pack were now pocked with homesteads and small settlements. Wolves faced greater competition for food than ever. Settlers brought milk cows, dairy cattle, and hogs to Tygart Valley, but the majority of their meat came from deer, elk, and bear.

Life around the high mountain meadows and mountain peaks during late spring, summer, and fall was little changed for the wolf pack. Blancus had developed into a successful leader and yet another litter of squirming wolf pups entered life deep within the safety of a previously used den during the spring of 1774. Blancus kept his pack on Cheat Mountain until late November that year, when deep snows and the scarcity of elk forced them down to the foothills lying adjacent to Tygart Valley. In spite of the settler's guns, white-tailed deer and elk remained abundant throughout the foothills, and Blancus consistently directed his nine-wolf pack on successful hunts.

The former solitude of the valley was now marked by the near-constant reverberations from axes, crosscut saws, hammers, cowbells, dinner bells, and laughing children. But these alien sounds occurred almost entirely during daylight hours. At night, few human-related sounds escaped the cabins and barns, but wolves were nevertheless constantly aware of the presence of these invaders. What their ears and eyes failed to detect, their noses readily identified.

Wood smoke from chimneys and smokehouses blanketed the valley and in so doing became a regular component of the bottomlands. Only a few months were required for Blancus to learn that the smoke permeating their environs was not from wind-driven wild fires, but from the many cabins and settlements.

Winds associated with wildfires carried distinct sounds and odors. The crackling and popping and roaring sounds of a raging wildfire were accompanied by a unique mélange of odors emanating from the various fuels, including dried grasses and leaves, resinous conifers, and the scorched bark of hardwoods. This gaseous-particulate composition was flavored by the earthy odors of green wood, mosses, half-rotted logs, lichens, and fungi.

By comparison, smoke drifting from the settler's chimneys carried odors of food. Originating from black iron skillets and kettles heated several times each day the scents mixed with cooking fire's smoke and were unmistakable. During winter, a pot of stew would simmer day and night, always warm when hungry men returned from cutting firewood or feeding livestock. While totally unlike the odors associated with a newly killed animal, or even those of week-old carrion, the cooking odors tempered the acrid odors created by burning firewood.

In addition to fireplaces, smokehouses operated day and night during all months of the year. Odors related to salt curing and smoke curing, the only means of preserving meats, were even less disturbing to wolves than were the smokes from chimneys. The odors, produced by drying strips of deer and elk meat, somewhat resembled those odors produced by a carcass drying in the sun.

On those crisp nights when a killing frost left the ground white, pockets of acrid wood smoke from flaming hardwoods in fireplaces settled within a few hundred yards of the cabins. In contrast, when the gusty winds of a cold front pushed through, the smoke spread more than one-half mile from the cabins, and the wolves detected it readily.

Blancus avoided the man-made structures until the winter of 1775, when he once again led his pack into the valley bottomlands—but only at night. The Haddan brothers were aware of the wolf pack through tracks and deer carcasses, both of which they regularly discovered during their hunting trips into the foothills. More ominously, the howling serenades brought fear to their households as they huddled around the fireplaces or nestled in their feather-tick mattresses under several woolen blankets.

The morning following one such frightful serenade, within 100 yards of their cabin, William Haddan and brother David pulled on the warmest boots and clothing they owned, loaded their rifles, and filled their back packs with deer jerky and biscuits. They planned to shoot a wolf.

The brothers set off in pursuit of the tracks in the snow. Temperatures were in the twenties and a foot of snow covered the ground. Wind gusts propelled fluffy, billowing snow across the valley floor, often restricting visibility. Shortly before noon, the Haddan brothers came across the carcass of a yearling elk. The brothers continued following wolf tracks that convened into a single well-trodden path within yards of the scene.

Following the kill, Blancus had led his pack three miles into the foothills, where they succumbed to the deep coma-like sleep triggered by bulging stomachs. As the sun's rays began to create small thermals from the nearby hemlocks, ground odors began to swirl. Although sound asleep, Blancus quickly awakened when the alarming scent of humans drifted to him. Low growls alerted the pack members and silently Blancus led them past the hemlocks and away from the humans. Though disturbed, the wolves exhibited no great fear. They had encountered human scent on many occasions, and had frequently witnessed them cutting firewood, feeding livestock, carrying buckets of water, and hunting deer. On numerous occasions the wolf pack had been shot at when they ventured out of the forest into the edge of an open field. However, most settlers were farmers rather than hunters. Short on practice and poorly equipped with crude muskets, they were fortunate to hit a deer or any similarly large target at a distance greater than 30-40 yards.

The encounter this day was to be different. The Haddan brothers both carried muzzleloaders, long-barreled firearms that would drastically change life on the frontier. These rifles were greatly superior to muskets because of grooves ingeniously cut inside the barrels that caused the lead bullet to undergo a stabilizing spin as the exploding black powder forced it out the barrel. With "rifling's" simple advance an accomplished hunter could hit a skillet-sized target at 100 yards.

Shortly after noon, with a red-tailed hawk screeching overhead, William and David split up. William moved parallel to the wolf tracks, about ten yards to the right, while David moved parallel on the left, but nearly 100 yards adjacent. He focused on the scene far ahead, hoping to spot an unsuspecting wolf, while at the same time using his peripheral vision to monitor William's travels. Blancus led his pack in a slow walk, unaware they were being tracked. Unfortunately for the wolves, the afternoon breezes shifted slightly and no longer carried human scent in their direction. After traveling over a mile with no human scent detected, Blancus selected an elevated knoll to resume their afternoon nap. Pack members curled into their normal nose-to-tail sleeping shapes, facing south in the sunlit snow, and were soon asleep.

William systematically stopped and waited while David stalked cautiously ahead. During one such sequence, David spotted five sleeping forms. Instinctively dropping to one knee, David emitted the call of a barred owl, who, who…who-whoo…who, who…who-whoooo. William likewise dropped to one knee and readied his rifle for firing. He primed the rifle and added fresh black powder to the pan. Both brothers began to slowly crawl on their bellies towards the wolves. Keeping behind tree trunks and downed logs they approached to within a long stone's throw of their targets.

The Haddans had hunted together on numerous occasions and had mastered a routine that enabled both brothers to get off a shot. The hunter on the left would fire at an animal on the left, while the hunter on the right would fire at an animal on the right. As David stopped, rested his rifle barrel over a fallen tree trunk, and took aim at one of the wolves, William followed suit, waiting for the report from David's rifle.

When David was confident that William was ready to shoot, he carefully sighted his rifle and slowly squeezed the trigger with his gloveless grip. Flint striking against steel threw a spark into the pan powder, which exploded and in turn ignited the main powder within the barrel. The expanding gases forced the lead bullet out of the barrel, spinning smoothly towards the target. William likewise squeezed the trigger and a second lead ball spun through the cold mountain air towards a sleeping wolf.

Daniel's bullet cut a deep furrow across the hip of a two-year old, dark gray female and within the same second of time, William's bullet entered Blancus' ribcage. The half-inch ball tore through the heart and out the other side of the ribcage. Before they could pour new powder and ram a lead ball into their rifle barrels the running wolves had disappeared from sight.

The wolf pack fled in panic through a stand of hemlocks and then out the rear in wild, ten-foot long plunges through the deep snow. Leaderless, they fled into the foothills and continued more than a mile up the mountainside before first stopping to rest. The single bullet wound to the two-year old wolf's hip had quit bleeding before the wolves covered 50 paces, but the pain persisted in the female's hip. Fortunately, she could easily reach the wound with her tongue and licked it steadily while the pack slowly reassembled. Amidst much face licking and whining, the wolves determined that all members were present—except Blancus.

Near panic ensued, as the wolves slowly realized they had lost their leader. Pack dedication to their leader and concern about his absence caused three of the young wolves to begin to retrace their tracks. Realizing their determination, the alpha female growled menacingly at them and all three returned to the pack. The alpha female was the oldest wolf in the pack, and had assumed some of the leader's duties even when Blancus was alive.

All life had drained from Blancus' body by the time the Haddan brothers reached his carcass. Anxiously, William examined the carcass and then attempted to hoist it. He managed to lift the front half from the snow, but the weight of nearly 110 pounds prevented him from raising the entire carcass. From nose to tip of tail, the lifeless form stretched over six feet in length. The brothers had never been so close to a wolf, nor had they seen and touched one. They examined the teeth, the claws, the dense fur, and the still-glaring yellow eyes. With their trophy stretched full-length in the snow, Daniel lay down in the snow alongside it to better estimate its length. The brothers would have liked to take the wolf intact back to their cabin, but realized it was not worth the effort to do so. Thus, William drew his hunting knife and carefully removed the head, paws, and luxurious pelt, exposing the naked, muscled carcass. This was the first wolf killed by one of the Tygart Valley settlers, but certainly would not be the last.

❧ *CHAPTER FOURTEEN* ❧
NATIVE UPRISINGS

The decade of the 1770s would be the bloodiest the valley had ever known, at least from the standpoint of human deaths. Wildlife avoided the settlers and their deadly firearms where possible. In contrast, Indians took a more direct approach to solving the problem of encroaching settlers—attack and kill. Shawnee, Delaware, and Mingo Indians had several villages at other locations throughout the Allegheny Mountains of western Virginia, but Tygart Valley had never supported permanent Indian villages. Nevertheless, numerous hunting parties visited the valley and many trading parties traveled through the region.

The Indian attacks in Tygart Valley during the mid-1770s were associated with major campaigns of the American Revolutionary War, which had become widespread and violent. Most Indian tribes west of the Alleghenies had been allies of the French during the French and Indian War of 1754-1759. The French desired to control all lands drained by the Ohio River to assure a constant supply of furs. In sharp contrast, the English wanted to control the lands for the purpose of supporting the thousands of settlers that were vital to their long-range plans.

The majority of the Indians preferred the French goals, which would have preserved the Indians' ancestral lands and their way of life. Unfortunately for the Indians, France lost the French and Indian War. Following the belated Treaty of Paris in 1763, France ceded their territory in North America to England. This resulted in a tidal wave of settlers crossing the Alleghenies.

As many had foreseen, the Indians attempted to stem the incursion and preserve their hunting grounds west of the Alleghenies. Several treaties subsequently signed by Indians granted the British the rights to lands west of the Allegheny Mountains. In some cases the Indians signing the treaties controlled the lands, but in other cases they did not. As would become the norm, treaty conditions were largely ignored by all parties: the Indians, the British government, and the American settlers.

In 1763, a loose confederation of several tribes joined together under the leadership of Pontiac, an Ottawa chief, and began attacking British forts. During that same period, small groups of Indians attacked lesser forts and isolated cabins of settlers throughout the western frontier. British armies responded and succeeded in destroying many Indian villages. Pontiac's War, as it was labeled, ended in 1766 when Chief Pontiac signed a peace treaty with the British at Fort Ontario in New York.

Even larger waves of settlers pushed into the lands west of the Alleghenies by the thousands during 1770-1774. And once again the Indians reacted as should have been expected. Attacks on settlers became widespread and successful.

Events took a strange turn when the American Revolutionary War began in 1775. Although the Indians by then had been fighting against the British redcoats for over 20 years, they were now convinced to join the English in war against the more offensive American colonists. War parties of several hundred Indians attacked Fort Pitt at Pittsburgh, Fort Henry at Wheeling, and Fort Randolph at Point Pleasant. But no armies of Indians invaded Tygart Valley. Regardless, lives of settlers in the region were at great risk. Barns and cabins were burned, while livestock were killed or stolen in retaliatory raids.

Following the deaths of their parents at the hands of Indians, the three Haddan brothers built a fort in 1774, less than one mile downstream from the mouth of Elkwater Creek. Currence's Fort was sited some nine miles downstream of Haddan's Fort, while Westfall's Fort was erected another ten miles further downstream, near the mouth of Files Creek (the site of the current town of Beverly).

Indian attacks on settlers, promoted by the British, accelerated during the mid-1770s and reached a peak in 1777. That year, known as the Year of the Terrible Sevens, was characterized by countless Indian attacks throughout western Virginia. Most attacks occurred during summer and early fall. The difficulty of traveling through winter snows and icy rivers discouraged Indian attacks then. Only when an unseasonably warm period arrived did Indians seek out the isolated white settlements during November or December. Such periods came to be known as Indian Summers by the settlers, who welcomed them with dread. Thus, despite their deep snows and freezing temperatures, winters in the central Appalachian Mountains brought temporary relief from Indian attacks.

In spite of the forts, several Indian attacks were successful. More than 100 settlers in and around Tygart Valley lost their lives to Indian retaliation, because many chose not to live in the forts for long periods of time. Darby Connally, plus his wife and children were killed in 1777. John McClain and John Nelson were killed in 1780 near the mouth of Elkwater Creek. James Wilmouth was killed in 1781 along the lower end of Shavers Fork. Joseph Kinnan, Sr. and three children were killed near the mouth of Elkwater Creek in 1791, and his wife was taken prisoner. A few days later, Frank Riffle and William Currence were killed in the hills separating Becky's Creek and Riffles Creek.

The Cheat Mountain wolf pack, led by new alpha male "Vulfe", was not directly impacted by the hostilities. Few settlers had moved onto Cheat Mountain, and Indians were rarely present during winter months when the wolves had shifted their home range to the bottomlands along the Tygart River. However, indirectly there were dramatic consequences of the Indian attacks.

Vulfe, a muscular adult with a silver coat contrasted by unusually dark gray feet, had become the alpha male two months after the death of Blancus. Once the disruptive, often violent, establishment of the new pack leader had been finalized, social and hunting behaviors closely resembled those prevalent under the previous pack leader. Vulfe proved to be a strong leader, but was not so cautious as previous alpha males.

One night in early November, after the pack had returned to the bottomlands, Vulfe was quietly leading his ten followers through a hardwood stand of gigantic sugar maples and black cherry. Temperatures were in the mid-sixties and early snows had melted from all areas except the north-facing shady pockets. This unseasonably warm spell had arrived two weeks earlier and, as the settlers had feared, was accompanied by the return of marauding Indians.

A three-quarter waxing moon illuminated the forest floor, and as the wolves quietly trailed the scent of a small herd of elk, their ghostly forms passed within 40 yards of six crouching Shawnee. The Indians had arrived from the lands west of the Ohio River three days earlier and had scouted several small settlements. They finally selected the small, isolated cabin of William Wamsley, which they planned to attack later that night. The Indians had spent the daylight hours in the foothills, their presence unsuspected by the settlers. As the moon neared its zenith, the Indians departed their temporary camp among a grove of hemlocks and began a slow, single-file trot towards the cabin.

The Indians had paused for a meal of jerky and a drink from the mountain stream when the wolves padded silently past. Vulfe and his pack had failed to detect the faint Indian odor and approached dangerously close to the resting marauders. Although the Indians' senses could not match those of the wolves, they had a major advantage. The wolves were moving while the Indians were motionless. On land, in almost every situation, non-mobile entities detect those on the move before they themselves are detected.

When the wolves were within 40 yards of the Indians one of them silently raised his long rifle and carefully aligned the sights onto the front shoulder of Vulfe. Being silver gray, he stood out amongst the dark shadows much more distinctly than did the dark haired wolves. The Indian swung the nearly four-foot long barrel smoothly and steadily. He was an excellent shot and had considerable practice with the muzzleloader, which he had obtained by trading beaver pelts with a British trader.

The Shawnee pushed his front sights six inches in front of the trotting wolf and tightened his finger on the trigger. Rather than pulling the trigger, however, he relaxed his grip and removed his finger from the trigger. He smiled at his companions and nodded his head. He was confident he could have sent a lead ball into the wolf had he wanted.

None of the Indians were surprised their companion had not fired. They knew that on a quiet night the sound of a rifle shot would carry several miles. Every person within the cabin would jerk awake. Preloaded weapons kept within reach of each bed would be hurriedly pointed out every window and shooting port and water would douse the fireplace flames. Inhabitants knew they would gain an advantage if they were in darkness while the attackers were rendered visible by moonlight. The small herd of elk being pursued by the wolves was headed for the remote corner of the hayfield situated nearly 300 yards from the William Wamsley cabin. As Vulfe and his pack entered the hayfield a wave of cold air flowing down the mountainside swept over them. Their scent thus carried towards the cabin, the calm and quiet was suddenly broken when Wamsley's two coonhounds erupted into a loud chorus. As the hounds became even more aroused by the scent their barking grew louder. Had the hounds not been chained they would have charged from the cabin porch after the wolves.

However, Wamsley had lost a prized hound the previous year when it broke its collar and plunged into the darkness in pursuit of a passing wolf pack. The next day, the settler found a patch of bloody snow, a few bones, and a piece of hide, all that remained of his hound. For this reason, all settlers kept their hounds securely chained on their cabin porch. In such a position they were safe from wolves and mountain lions, but could detect most Indians who attempted to stalk close to the cabin.

The approaching Indians crept close to the edge of the hayfield, but halted their approach upon hearing the hound's baying. After much discussion and now aware of the Wamsley dogs, they decided to halt their planned attack and wait for a cloudy night when they would not be so easily detected. Vulfe likewise decided to abandon his hunt of the now alert elk and led the pack away from the cabin and barking hounds.

Later that night they chanced upon a feeding white-tailed deer and after a short chase brought it to the ground. Vulfe, as usual, had made the initial charge and the force of his muscular frame knocked the deer to the ground. Before it had time to regain footing, Vulfe locked his jaws onto its right-rear leg and the alpha female locked her jaws onto the deer's throat. Death came quickly and pack members gorged themselves on venison.

❧ CHAPTER FIFTEEN ❧
RANDOLPH COUNTY

In 1787, another significant change occurred in the Tygart Valley. Randolph County was created. Much of western Virginia fell within the region previously known as West Augusta—an area seriously considered for recognition as the 14th American colony. In 1744, Augusta County, including that huge area stretching from the Allegheny Mountains to the Ohio River, was created. In 1769, that singular area was subdivided. The northern half, which contained the region that would eventually become West Virginia, retained the name, Augusta County. The southern half was named Botetourt County. Further subdivision of Augusta County occurred in the history-making year of 1776, with the creation of Monongalia, Ohio, and Yohogania counties.

Earlier that year, several petitions from residents of Tygart Valley were submitted to the Virginia Assembly in Richmond requesting protection and the formation of a more accessible government office. They argued that 250 families lived in "Tigers" Valley and they needed to cross eight mountains to reach Staunton, Virginia. As a result of these petitions and numerous other requests, Harrison County was formed from the southern portion of Monongalia County in 1784, and in 1787 Randolph County was carved out of Harrison County. Most of Cheat Mountain and Tygart Valley were located within the boundaries of Randolph County.

All of this political maneuvering was largely irrelevant to the wolves of Cheat Mountain. However, one of the first acts of the newly-created Randolph County Court was to establish a bounty on wolves. In 1787 settlers could claim a bounty of $1.00 for every wolf scalp or hide they turned in. Sheriff Jacob Westfall, Jr. typically applied the bounty money towards what the settler owed in taxes.

Around 1785, as numbers of elk and white-tailed deer continued to dwindle, Vulfe began to investigate certain pastures under the cover of darkness. The scent of the settlers' livestock was strange but fascinating. While it somewhat resembled elk, the wolves easily distinguished domestic animals from wild. On several winter nights the wolves passed cautiously through a split rail fence and investigated the cattle from a distance. Most were full-grown and appeared larger than the buffalo that wandered through the Valley during summer. Smaller livestock had been moved into barns in November and thus were not visible to the wolves.

In most such encounters, the fenced in cattle had exhibited a habit of herding together and milling nervously about while the wolves moved on in search of a deer or elk. However, one night in early December of 1786, Vulfe discovered a young Jersey heifer owned by John Warwick that was grazing in a hayfield with two large draft horses. Every morning, Warwick threw down several pitchforks of hay from a tall, pear-shaped haystack to the heifer and horses. The farmer planned to move the animals into a barn where they would be fed from the haymow when snows and cold weather became severe. Warwick had already moved his milk cows into the barn, where they would remain throughout the long winter months. Without a kill in three nights, Vulfe's incautious attitude drove the wolves to attack the heifer. Although the heifer weighed more than a yearling elk, the wolf attack lasted less than three minutes before the Jersey was brought sprawling to the ground. Wolves tore at the bloody red meat and became gorged before the carcass could be stripped clean. Following their feast, Vulfe eyed the horses dispassionately, as he led his wolf into the foothills where they spent the day digesting their meal.

The pack killed five other beef cattle that winter at various farms. Livestock were one of the most valuable properties owned by the settlers and the death of even one animal could prove a catastrophic loss. However, despite settlers' constant fear of predators, they had little spare time to pursue wolves. As usual, cutting firewood, milking cows, hauling water, and hundreds of other demanding chores occupied nearly every hour of daylight.

John Warwick owned 69 head of cattle in 1787, more than any other settler in Randolph County. Now familiar with the land and the livestock, Vulfe killed yet another of Warwick's Jersey cows in late November. The cow's injured front leg had doomed it as an easy target for the pack. They managed to separate her from others of the herd and when she became trapped in one corner of the rail fence they brought the 700-pound animal to the ground. Although the wolves had not eaten in two days, they were able to consume only a fraction of the available meat.

Upon discovering the cow's carcass and the wolf tracks, Warwick spat tobacco juice on the ground and began salvaging what was left of the meat. He removed the heifer's tongue, the two front shoulders, the lower portion of one hind leg, and the hide. All other parts had been consumed or so damaged he was unwilling to feed them to his family. Although he had killed and butchered two of his yearling steers in late October and his smokehouse was overflowing, no meat was allowed to go to waste.

Later that day he and his neighbor, James McLane, used a draft horse to drag what remained of the cow carcass outside the split rail fence. They strategically selected a spot where they could be concealed within a stand of dense hemlocks yet still have an open shot at a returning wolf.

Though each wolf had consumed more than ten pounds of meat, by early evening they were once again ready to eat. Sensing the impatience of the pack members, and feeling early hunger pangs himself, Vulfe gave the hunting command and all members excitedly came together for the pre-hunt rituals. Group howling, face licking, and excited prancing occurred as usual. At dusk, Vulfe led the pack down off the mountainside to the cow carcass.

Warwick and neighbor McLane, who owned a muzzleloader and was a crack shot, had secluded themselves behind two separate piles of fresh-cut hemlock branches. Warwick had both a musket and 12-gauge shotgun but realized he would be unlikely to hit a wolf at distances over 50 yards. In contrast, McLane was confident of hitting a wolf at 100 yards with his muzzleloader, if he had time to aim and light to see by. The moon was a waxing crescent in its first quarter and threw only dim light over the landscape, but he smiled as he envisioned the wolves silhouetted against the snow. Bundled in layers of ticking, wool, and broadcloth, and wrapped in wool blankets, the men sat patiently.

Barely two hours later, a faint series of howls brought knowing looks from the chilled hunters. The cold was forgotten as the men caught their first glimpse of a wolf's movement some half an hour later. Vulfe, appearing as a moving shadow, trotted confidently from the nearby woods towards the carcass. Behind him, in single file, came nine other pack members. The men had avoided walking near the wolves' tracks and had positioned their shooting blind over 50 yards from where the tracks entered the woods. No breeze stirred that night, and the men's scent was not detected by the wolves. Vulfe, encountering the kill's scent sooner than expected, stopped just 100 yards from the carcass. He sat on his haunches and cautiously surveyed the scene before him. Smelling only whiffs of the meat, he began to anticipate the meal. The wolves had not yet learned to avoid humans and their settlements. They had been shot at a few times, but only a handful had been hit. However, the pack would soon learn the consequences of approaching too close to humans.

Vulfe rose from his haunches and trotted downhill towards the edge of the hayfield. As the pack approached the carcass, McLane slipped his hand from the mitt and slid his muzzleloader across a hemlock limb, steadying its sights onto the carcass. It was much too dark for him to target an individual wolf, thus he planned to shoot into the pack. Warwick would wait patiently until McLane shot, firing the musket simultaneously, and then hope one of the frightened wolves would run near enough for him to shoot it with the remaining shotgun.

As the arriving shadows converged on their previous-night's kill, sounds of snarling and growling reached the men's ears, and McLane pulled the trigger, the gun's roar nearly masking the blast from Warwick's shot. In near panic, the wolves erupted from the carcass and began a chaotic retreat. It was not possible for the men to determine if a dead wolf lay alongside the cow carcass, but McLane attempted to reload his long rifle as wolves sped past. As Vulfe passed 50 yards from Warwick he fumbled to fire both barrels of his 12-gauge shotgun at the alpha male. The black powder explosions sent nearly two-dozen, pea-sized lead pellets spreading.

All wolves quickly vanished from sight and Warwick and McLane cautiously moved to the cow carcass. Disappointed to find no dead wolves they returned to their cabins, tired, cold, and sore. They believed it was much too dark and much too dangerous to attempt to track the wolves that night.

The two men returned anxiously early the next morning after feeding their livestock, and began tracking the wolves. Warwick became energized upon finding blood in the tracks. The blood had spurted from three small pellet holes in Vulfe's hip. The wounded wolf had reached the shelter of the woods before the seriousness of his injury became apparent. One pellet had passed with little consequence through the thigh muscle, but the second had lodged alongside the head of the thighbone. The third lead pellet had caused more serious damage. It had passed through the major aorta extending down the hind leg and resulted in the blood trailing on the snow. The faster Vulfe ran and the farther he jumped, the more blood was pumped out of the wound. Before he had run one mile he began to falter. He fell to the rear of the pack, slowed significantly, and then staggered to the ground.

Warwick and McLane followed the blood spatters from Vulfe's wound through the woods for nearly 15 minutes. Much to their disappointment, the red drops became farther apart, and smaller in size. They concluded the wolf was not seriously injured and would probably escape, but ten minutes later they reconsidered. Much to their surprise, and elation, they saw a wolf in the snow 60 yards ahead. They separated, moved to opposite sides of the wolf's tracks and raised their weapons in readiness. With the wolf so near, both men feared it would suddenly jump from the snow and bound away through the woods. When there was no sign of life they moved closer. The wolf was dead, that was certain. What they couldn't know was that the life of another alpha male had come to an end.

After a rapid gallop of nearly two miles following the black powder explosions, the pack became aware of their leader's absence. Rather than return to the cow carcass, "Grisa", the brownish-black alpha female, led the pack on a rapid gallop up the valley. They fled 12 miles before stopping. Grisa was satisfied that all pack members except Vulfe were present, and they had apparently escaped the attack without harm. She did not notice one of the yearling females licking constantly at her left hip. The young female would survive but would carry the small scar and, more importantly, the fear of cow carcasses, for the rest of her life.

Grisa moved her pack south of Elkwater Creek and they remained at the southernmost extremities of their range throughout that winter. They avoided settlers' cabins and all other sites bearing human scent. The remaining members of the pack accepted the alpha female's leadership with only minor conflicts occurring.

One of Grisa's first tasks following her acceptance as pack leader was scent-marking the boundaries of their territory. Vulfe had done the majority of the marking in previous years, but other pack members added their scent at every location where their leader urinated. Now Grisa was driven to leave her scent every 50 yards or so along the pack's southern boundary.

Raised leg urination, as done by males, usually marked an object a foot above ground level, thus facilitating dispersal of the scent by wind. Grisa, being a female, relied on squat urination. Upon noting Grisa urinating on an object, the two-year old males always utilized raised-leg urination to scent mark the same or another nearby object.

Grisa and her pack would occasionally hear other wolves howl, and this drove them to increase their scent marking. Howls could be heard from a distance of five miles, thus each pack was constantly aware of the presence of another. In most situations, packs respected the territorial boundaries of other packs and conflicts were rare.

The impressive silver-gray hide of Vulfe became the first wolf turned in to Sheriff Westfall for bounty in 1787. Word of the bounties encouraged more settlers to engage in wolf hunting and, as a result, 13 wolves were killed in Randolph County in 1788 and another eight in 1789. One hundred eighty-five wolves were killed during the 1790s and turned in to the Randolph County sheriff. The pursuit of wolves had begun in earnest.

From the manic efforts to kill wolves, it was as if the settlers needed an enemy after the last marauding Indian retreated across the Ohio River. The wolf was a fitting nemesis. Their group attacks, like those of stealthy Appalachian tribes, came without warning, but usually with deadly effect. Talk around the dinner tables almost always came around to wolves. Talk at any get-together of two or more farmers inevitably covered the best techniques to kill wolves. The merits of rifles, shotguns, traps, pitfalls, dogs, and poisons were debated endlessly.

Two hundred and nineteen wolves were killed during 1800-1809, 351 during 1810-1819, 379 during 1820-1829, and 229 during 1830-1839. Hundreds more bounty kills would occur in Randolph County during the ensuing mid-1800s.

Several of the wolf scalps turned in for bounties were most likely not collected in Randolph County, but instead in adjacent counties. Also of relevance, Randolph County contained what is now Tucker County—that county being formed from the northeastern portion of Randolph County in 1856. Regardless of where they were actually killed, more than 1,000 wolves were slaughtered and turned in for bounties in Randolph County during the 40-year period from 1790 to 1830. Thirty of these wolves, killed in various decades, were members of the Cheat Mountain pack. Many were pups, including six killed during June of 1824.

Joseph Crouch had discovered a wolf den near the headwaters of Becky's Creek while searching for ginseng. This tributary of the Tygart River originated high on Cheat Mountain and joined with the main river three miles upstream of the Huttonsville settlement. While he traced a damp, north-facing hillside, Crouch spotted the month-old pups playing outside their den. The adults, including the pup's mother, were away hunting vulnerable deer fawns. Crouch slipped away unseen, but returned the next day with a shovel, a pickaxe, and one large foxhound. The bounty, payable for adults or young, was a strong incentive for his efforts and usurped the lure of the medicinal plant he had been searching for.

Crouch dug steadily through the sandy loam soil for two hours before taking a break to eat six pieces of dried beef and a biscuit. In another hour he reached the enlarged den. Dropping the shovel, he put on heavy leather gloves and a thick leather coat to protect against bites or scratches from the pups. While stretched out full length on the ground the young man stuck his right arm deep into the den.

The mother wolf had returned while Crouch was digging and waited anxiously behind a fallen hemlock tree, 30 yards distant. As Crouch pulled out a squealing pup and held it at arm's length, the mother wolf whined and inched a few feet towards the man. When Crouch smashed the pup against a boulder and then crushed its head with the heel of his heavy leather boots, the mother wolf whined pitifully and crawled even closer. The wolf was downwind and hidden in a clump of tall blueberry bushes.

As the man prodded inside the cavity with a long stick, a second pup bolted out of the den but was quickly grabbed by the hound. The pup had time for only two quick squeals before the hound crushed its ribcage. Crouch took the pup from the hound and placed it in a heavy leather pack with the first dead pup. While the young man again probed in the den the mother wolf crawled to within 15 yards. A low growl escaped from deep within her chest. She crouched with all four feet beneath her and tensed her muscles, as if preparing to charge.

The mother wolf stared intently while four more of her pups were pulled from the den and crushed one at a time against a boulder. Although the wolf whined and growled the entire time, she made no effort to interfere.

No Cheat Mountain wolf had ever attacked a human. A pack would not hesitate to attack an elk or a buffalo, a black bear or a mountain lion. Thousands of farm animals were attacked and killed, but human lives apparently were not in danger. Regardless, most early settlers viewed wolves as their greatest enemy. The Appalachian frontier abounded with tales of wolves attacking humans, but these have never been substantiated.

As the sun dipped low, Joseph Crouch shouldered the leather pack containing the six pups and began his trek homeward. Bounties for the six would total enough to buy a new rifle, several boxes of ammunition, and another foxhound.

When Crouch faded out of sight, the mother wolf hurried to the destroyed den and began a fruitless search for her pups. She remained near the den for five days, but then permanently abandoned the site. No other pups would be born to females of the pack that summer, and only five individuals would accompany the alpha male that winter.

Appalachian timber wolf populations during the late 1700s and early 1800s were drastically reduced because of bounties, but even more so by the loss of their hunting grounds. The human population of the somewhat typical Randolph County was 951 in 1790, but had grown to 1,826 by 1800 and to 5,000 by 1830. Areas that had once provided hunting grounds for timber wolves were being decimated. Gardens, croplands, pastures, and hayfields replaced forests and natural meadows. In addition, roads bisected many of the remaining forests and meadows. Wolves were forced into the last vestiges of Appalachia's wilderness.

EDWIN DARYL MICHAEL

❦ *CHAPTER SIXTEEN* ❧
THE LAST BUFFALO

Wolves were not the only wildlife declining in numbers. Elk had become a rarity in Randolph County by 1825, and white-tailed deer numbers were steadily on the decline. Even more ominous for the wolf pack, no buffalo would be seen in Randolph County after 1825.

Two hunters were waiting for deer at a saltlick in Webster County, which abutted Randolph County to the south, when they were startled to spot a buffalo cow and her calf approaching the lick. They could not believe their eyes, but there was no doubt they were buffalo. Ill-equipped to kill such ponderous beasts, the men hurriedly returned to their cabins, gathered their hounds, notified several neighbors, and set off in search of the alluring cow and her half-grown calf.

Upon returning to the saltlick, the small hunting party released their hounds at the buffalo tracks and the canines set off with deep-chested bawls and excited barks, pulled forward by the buffalo's scent. The hounds caught up with their quarry on Valley Fork of the Elk River. They quickly surrounded the frightened calf and prevented its escape, but the cow plunged down the mountainside and escaped from view. The hunters immediately shot the calf and urged the hounds after the 1,000-pound cow.

The wild-eyed buffalo ran headlong through rhododendron and spruce thickets, jumping over downed logs and smashing down small trees in its frantic flight. Late that afternoon the hounds caught up with the weary cow and surrounded her as she made a stand within a small clump of large hemlocks, not far from the settlement of Valley Head. The hounds continued to bark fiercely and charge the cow, but none were brave enough to inflict a bite. This change in the dogs' clamor urged the hunters to move even faster though the rugged terrain, and they arrived within an hour. It was obvious the cow was exhausted and could run no further, thus the equally taxed hunters sat around laughing and examining the strange-shaped bovine.

None of those hunters that autumn day in 1825 had ever seen a buffalo, and they were most curious. This was a monumental day—as no one else would ever see another wild one in the region. As darkness neared, the hunters drew straws to determine who would have the opportunity to shoot the helpless cow—the last buffalo reported in Virginia (or West Virginia).

Whether other buffalo roamed unseen through the Allegheny Mountains after 1825, none were ever reported, nor is it consequential. An epoch of immeasurable natural richness had ended at Valley Head, near the headwaters of the Tygart River. The symbolic significance of the site as an early milestone in the modern-day history of eastern wildlife was missed.

$\backsim$ *CHAPTER SEVENTEEN* $\backsim$
STAUNTON-TO-PARKERSBURG TURNPIKE

One rainy day in early July of 1839, "Castana", the reigning alpha male of the pack, was startled from his mid-day nap by the sounds of loud shouting, then by multiple whacks of axes against tree trunks. Although such sounds were not welcome, the wolf pack had become accustomed to human-created disturbances. Every year, for nearly eight decades, white men had passed through the territory of the wolf pack. At first it had been explorers and settlers on foot. Later they traveled by horseback and with small pack trains. By the late 1700s, wagons were hauling settlers, their large families, and their total earthly belongings across Cheat Mountain. Although the wagons closely followed trails previously traveled by buffalo herds, considerable forest clearing was necessary to accommodate the wagon beds. Every group of wagons carried axes and crosscut saws, tools put to use every daylight hour of the cross-country adventure.

Such wagon-borne travelers rarely took time to hunt while crossing Cheat Mountain, although a few youngsters were sent in search of squirrels while older men cleared the wagon trail. Wolves and other wildlife had been frightened by the first black powder explosions from muskets during the mid-1700s, but because they suffered no pain, they became somewhat accustomed to the strange noises. Likewise, because the sounds of axes and crosscut saws were accompanied by no negative impacts, the wolves did not react in panic.

However, by the early 1800s wolves had learned to associate such alien forest sounds with potential danger. Castana was especially alarmed that summer day in 1839 because the human shouts were unusually loud.

The group creating this most-recent disturbance was a surveying crew busily engaged in laying out the route of the Staunton-to-Parkersburg Turnpike. In 1826, the General Assembly of Virginia had authorized the construction of a turnpike from the Shenandoah Valley to the Ohio River. They believed the new road would improve living conditions on the western frontier and increase population. The anticipated settlement of western Virginia promised to result in the harvest of the vast timber resources and development of the fertile agricultural lands.

Beginning at Staunton, various groups of surveyors had followed the many buffalo trails into the wilderness reaches of the Allegheny Mountains. Beginning at an elevation of about 1,000 feet, the route swung around the north end of Great North Mountain and crossed the headwaters of Calfpasture River, elevation 1,900 feet. From there it climbed Shenandoah Mountain at 3,000 feet in elevation, and then crossed Cowpasture River and Bullpasture River. Continuing west-by-northwest it strategically slipped through a gap on Jack Mountain at about 3,700 feet elevation, and dropped down into the gentle valley and the village of Monterey. Here it crossed the shallow headwaters of the South Branch of the Potomac River before climbing the east flank of Allegheny Mountain. After reaching an elevation of 4,200 feet, the surveyed route dropped down to the East Fork of the Greenbrier River, which it followed to the settlement of Bartow. Once it had crossed the West Fork of the Greenbrier River it began the challenging ascent of Cheat Mountain itself, reaching an elevation of 4,400 feet.

The surveyors had made steady progress in charting a course through the valley pastures and hardwood forests of oak, cherry, and chestnut. The existing trail, which had been followed by thousands of earlier settlers, was easily traversed and offered little resistance to the surveying parties. However, at those sites where it was necessary to modify the route to maintain a grade of less than four degrees, as directed by the Virginia General Assembly, the surveying party frequently encountered serious roadblocks. Young spruce thickets, with their dead branches extending nearly to the ground, required considerable whacking with axes to clear the surveyor's path. But no barrier was as difficult or as exasperating as the "laurel hells." These dense thickets, actually rhododendron rather than mountain laurel, presented the most difficult barriers the surveyor's axe men would encounter along the entire 200-mile turnpike. Impossible to walk through or crawl under, the tough, axe-deflecting stems of rhododendron created hellish conditions that required hours of axe work to clear a narrow opening.

Conditions atop Cheat Mountain were especially troublesome for the surveyors, as they frequently encountered bogs, as well as the tangles of rhododendron interspersed with stands of balsam fir and red spruce. Hours were required for the axe men to produce a narrow tunnel through or around such natural barriers that would permit sighting by survey transits.

Alerted by such commotion, Castana led his pack to an overlook above Shavers Fork where they were able to study the surveying party. From 200 yards, the wolves could easily hear the axes and curses of the men and see the shuddering leaves above, as they attempted to clear the trail. When Castana had determined the surveyors presented no immediate danger he calmly led his pack several miles up the river. There they napped during the remaining daylight hours before commencing their nightly hunt.

The surveying party continued its slow progress across Cheat Mountain and by August had begun the descent to the Tygart River. After crossing the river and passing through the Huttonsville settlement they reached Beverly, thus completing the most difficult, and most important section. During the summer of 1839, other surveying parties had been busy laying out the western section of the turnpike from Beverly to Parkersburg.

Although original planning for the turnpike had been completed in 1826, funding was not authorized until 1838. Reviews of earlier plans and numerous revisions of specific sections of the route delayed the work of surveyors. Final plans specified a width of no more than 20 feet nor less than 15. Grade would not exceed four degrees, although it was later determined that four and one-half degrees would be acceptable in a few sites. Actual construction of the turnpike began in late spring 1840.

The sounds of giants trees thundering to the earth were detected by the wolves at distances of nearly four miles. The loggers were the first of several construction crews that would spend the summer and early fall on Cheat Mountain. Pack trains of mules accompanied the loggers, carrying saws, axes, files, wedges, tents, cooking equipment, whiskey, and all camping equipment and supplies necessary to support the loggers. At times, there were six logging crews working on Cheat Mountain, each responsible for a 20-mile section. The size of each group ranged from as few as 20 men to as many as 40.

Slowly the crews moved across Cheat Mountain, some days felling trees over stretches reaching only 100 yards. Other days they covered nearly one-half mile. Twelve days were typically required for a crew of ten men to clear the 2.4 acres that encompassed one mile of roadway. The 20-foot swath inched inexorably across the rugged terrain.

Following closely on the heels of the loggers came the teams of oxen and their handlers. Their job was to pull the felled trees away from the 20-foot swath and into the adjacent forest. Men with crosscut saws and double-bitted axes reduced the fallen giants, some forty inches in diameter, to manageable sections.

Immediately behind them came the road crews themselves, primarily Irish laborers. These crews included the blasters and the teamsters responsible for controlling the large shovel-like scoops pulled by teams of horses or mules. Loggers had cut a few of the smaller trees at ground level with double-bitted axes, low enough that wagons could easily pass over top. However, most remaining stumps were so high they needed to be removed completely so a relatively smooth roadbed would result. It was nearly impossible for loggers to cut through a large tree at ground level. Large stumps and boulders needed to be blasted before they could be removed. Nitroglycerin made this possible. Otherwise, much of the road would have weaved around trees throughout much of its route.

When the roadbed was finally smoothed and leveled, or at least relatively so, the bridge building crew arrived. Lemuel Chenoweth, the most famous of all eastern bridge builders in the early-1800s, had designed bridges to cross various rivers and streams. One of the most difficult to construct was that over Shavers Fork River atop Cheat Mountain. The threats of high water, ice jams, and deep snows required the bridge be built high enough above the normal stream to prevent ice from tearing it out when spring floods occurred.

Cheat Bridge, as it would later be known, was to be a covered bridge, as were bridges at Beverly, Philippi, and two others crossing the Tygart River. Chenoweth believed this would greatly increase the life of the bridge by keeping the supports and underpinnings dry.

Although recently cut logs could be used to form the basic bridge supports, the sides and roof were best constructed of mill-sawn boards. There were no sawmills atop Cheat Mountain and none within 20 miles. Thus, construction of the covered portion of Cheat Bridge was delayed until the road was completed from Monterey to the top of Cheat Mountain. Wagons were then used to transport boards cut to the proper length to complete the roof and sides.

By midsummer, the wolf pack found their summer hunting territory atop Cheat Mountain sharply bisected by an almost constant corridor of human activity. Although they crossed the construction zone a few nights, the never-ending sounds and odors were such a distraction to the wolves and their prey that Castana moved the pack to the southern end of their territory and remained there until heavy snows forced construction crews to depart in late October.

Portions of the turnpike immediately west of Staunton were open to wagon travel in 1841 and construction across Cheat Mountain to Beverly (current US Route 250) was completed in 1843. The section westward from Beverly to Weston was completed in 1845, while that from Weston to Parkersburg was completed in 1848. The final bridge on the turnpike was open to wagon traffic in 1850. Although the major construction activities atop Cheat Mountain ceased with the completion of the covered bridge, the silence of a pristine forest did not return—and never would.

Most turnpike travelers crossed Cheat Mountain during daylight hours without stopping, other than brief rests to allow their horses to drink. Many even continued travel at night when moonlight was sufficient to illuminate their route. However, the howls of wolves, screams of mountain lions, and plethora of other eerie night sounds caused a dilemma for many travelers. Should they continue traveling after dark so they might get off the mountain with no further delay, or should they stop, build a great roaring fire, and spend the night? Was the risk greater while traveling or while camping? Few of those venturing from the eastern shore had ever encountered a wolf or a mountain lion and they knew nothing of the dangers associated with these predators.

Castana was aware of many of the overnight campers, but avoided their fires. However, in August 1843 one party of travelers was in no hurry to cross Cheat Mountain and was observed several times by the wolves. Traveling by horseback, with tents, food, and other supplies carried by packhorses, two of the men spent every available daylight hour combing through the forest. Their unusual behavior intrigued the wolves, and on several days the animals observed them curiously from rocky promontories. William Sullivant and Dr. Asa Gray, a prominent Harvard botanist, were exploring western Virginia to identify new or unusual plants. Five assistants accompanied them to handle the packhorses, cooking, and other camp chores. Each morning after breakfast, the two botanists would leave camp and tromp through the forest and bogs examining and collecting plant specimens. Although the men never saw the wolves, they heard their howling on several nights.

A steady stream of traffic was using the road by summer of 1849. Wagons, drawn by teams of two, four, or even six horses or oxen, crossed Cheat Mountain daily. Travel was difficult along the rutted, rocky, muddy road, but was made somewhat more bearable by the prominent blooms of rhododendron, the shrub that had only recently frustrated road crews. July was the peak blooming season for the most spectacular of all mountain shrubs—rhododendron or "great laurel." When exposed to direct sunlight, this evergreen shrub that preferred damp woods grew 20 feet tall and bore showy flower clusters ranging from white to pink.

Stagecoaches were less frequent than wagons, but more consistent in their times of arrival. At least twice daily a stagecoach crossed the mountain, one traveling east to west while the other traveled west to east. Stages departed Staunton every Monday, Wednesday, and Friday, at one o'clock in the afternoon. Stages from Parkersburg likewise departed on Monday, Wednesday, and Friday, but at four o'clock in the afternoon. Departure times were set to accommodate arrival before dark at an inn that would provide lodging and meals. Travel time over the 220-mile route was three to four days, with no night travel. Overnight lodging and meals were available at Monterey and Hightown, Virginia, Traveller's Repose, near the current town of Bartow, at Barton's Tavern near the headwaters of Riffle Creek, and at Beverly.

Tollgates were constructed at various points along the road. These consisted of a heavy post set in the ground and a long pole, or "pike", extending across the road. All travelers were required to stop and pay the toll before proceeding. Upon paying, the pike was turned by the tollgate operator to allow passage, thus the name, "turnpike", emerged. Tolls were five cents for a man on horseback, 20 cents for a two-wheel carriage, 45 cents for a four-wheel carriage, and 55 cents for a wagon with four or more horses.

Wolves returned to the Shavers Fork Area during the summer of 1849, and gradually adjusted to the wagons, stagecoaches, and horseback riders. Prey animals, such as white-tailed deer, beaver, rabbits, and wild turkey remained nearly as abundant as before the turnpike was constructed, although they shunned the areas near the road.

The pack regularly crossed the new road, hunting on both the north and south sides. In addition to wagons and stagecoaches, droves of horses, mules, cattle, sheep, hogs, and domestic turkeys were regularly pushed across Cheat Mountain. The livestock droppings that dotted the turnpike were a great attraction to the wolves, and they spent hours investigating these strange odors.

The turnpike and its travelers were less of a problem to the wolf pack in winter. Stagecoaches were used to carry mail to Tygart Valley and towns to the west, but deep snows often stopped travel. The cost for delivering a piece of mail was 25 cents, with the fee paid by the person receiving the mail.

Because of road conditions and weather, mail delivery was not always reliable. One February, the postmaster general in Washington, D.C., received complaints that mail was not being delivered along the turnpike. He demanded to know why the stagecoach driver had not made his regular trips and was told, "If the floodgates of hell were to open, and it were to rain fire and brimstone for six straight weeks, it wouldn't melt all the snow on Cheat Mountain, so if the people of Parkersburg want their damned old mail, let them come and get it."

Although the passing travelers posed no immediate threat to the wolves, the road did improve access to the plateau atop Cheat Mountain, and a few settlers established farms there in the 1850s. These had a minor impact on the wolves, as settlers and wolves competed for the same deer, and the rare surviving elk that visited the mountain meadows.

❦ *CHAPTER EIGHTEEN* ❧
CIVIL WAR

In 1861, a relatively minor event occurred about 40 miles down the Tygart River from the wolf pack. The first land battle of the Civil War took place at Philippi on June 3. General McClellan and his Union troops defeated a small contingent of Confederate troops at the Philippi covered bridge. This would eventually cause the demise of the Cheat Mountain wolf pack.

The Staunton-to-Parkersburg Turnpike was critical to both the Confederate and Union armies. Whichever side controlled the Turnpike would control access to the Ohio River. Movements of troops and supplies from the Shenandoah Valley to the Ohio Valley proved essential to winning the war. Also, the Union leaders realized the importance of driving out those Confederate forces west of Allegheny Mountains. In so doing, the Union could better protect the Baltimore and Ohio Railroad. The Confederates established forts along the Greenbrier River near the current town of Bartow (Camp Bartow) in 1861, and atop Allegheny Mountain (Camp Allegheny) in the summer of the same year. Those wolf packs living atop Allegheny Mountain suffered displacement as a result of these forts being constructed. Later, when Union forces attacked Camp Bartow and Camp Allegheny, local wolf packs were again impacted.

That same summer of 1861, Union troops constructed Camp Elkwater in the Tygart Valley and Camp Milroy (also known as Cheat Summit Fort) atop Cheat Mountain. Cheat Summit Fort was constructed near the middle of the Cheat Mountain wolf pack's summer territory. Situated one-half mile south of the Shavers Fork covered bridge (now known as Cheat Bridge), the fort was erected on a relatively flat plateau of approximately 20 acres that had comprised the White Farm. While much of the site had been cleared previously for farming, fort construction required clearing hundreds of additional acres to obtain logs for the walls, blockhouse, cabins, barns, and associated structures. Walls, consisting of solid vertical logs, were 14 feet in height and 8 feet wide at their bases.

Soldiers from Cheat Summit Fort also cleared hundreds of acres of forest on each side of the turnpike, to better permit firing at any Confederate troops that might attempt to pass. Union forces brought in a small steam-powered sawmill and hundreds of spruce trees were cut to produce boards for doors, tables, chairs, beds, cabinets, and stalls for livestock.

Designed by Brigadier General Robert Milroy and General George McClellan, the completed fort was thought to be resistant to artillery, cavalry, and infantry attacks. More than 5,000 soldiers resided at the fort at various times.

Confederate troops, under the direction of General Robert E. Lee, attacked Cheat Summit Fort on September 12, 1861. Numerous skirmishes occurred over the next two days, but the Confederates were forced to withdraw from the area.

Once again the pack was driven from its summer range. "Venali", the current reigning alpha male, led his pack to the southern extremities of their territory, much as had Castana when construction of the Staunton-to-Parkersburg Turnpike occurred 12 years earlier. Areas near the headwaters of Shavers Fork River were much more rugged and less conducive to farming than were areas throughout the plateaus near Cheat Bridge, and thus supported fewer settlers. But of greater importance to the wolves, there were no major roads crossing Cheat Mountain farther south.

The Civil War and the related construction of Cheat Summit Fort did more ultimately to extirpate the Cheat Mountain wolf pack than any other single event. Hundreds of prime acres of wolf habitat were destroyed or rendered useless due to the construction and maintenance of the forts. Thousands of trees were cut to obtain firewood, which was almost as valuable as food.

Winter temperatures on Cheat Mountain were frequently below zero, and an endless pile of firewood was needed to make life bearable for troops. At 4,000 feet elevation, Cheat Summit Fort was the highest Union Camp built during the Civil War. The high elevation resulted in severe weather during even non-winter months. A heavy freeze occurred on June 5, 1861 and all crops in the region froze. Snow fell on August 13, 1861, and several horses froze to death that September.

Forest fires were also prevalent during the war. The largest single burn extended along the summit and sides of Cheat Mountain, through Randolph, Pendleton, Grant, and Tucker counties. The fire, which spread from the camp of Confederate Scouts at Roaring Plains of Randolph County, resulted in wholesale destruction of thousands of acres of red spruce. This fire and countless others during the Civil War contributed significantly to the reduction of available prey animals for the few remaining wolves.

Thousands of soldiers, both Confederate and Union, wandered throughout Cheat Mountain during the war. Numerous deer, a few elk, and several wolves were shot by soldiers. However, the biggest impact on wolf packs was the disruption of daily behavior and associated hunts. Rarely did a wolf pack go longer than two days without encountering humans or their repugnant scent. In this manner, the Civil War grew into one long, major disruption of the mountain ecosystem. Never again would packs of wolves routinely pursue deer and elk. Brought on by the division of a country and the subsequent resolution, the war would result in insurmountable pressure for timber wolves to flee centuries old habitats. An era had ended!

For the people who lived in the region, however, a promising new era had begun. Following the secession of Virginia from the Union, most state delegates from west of the Allegheny Mountains declared their independence and set up a new government—the Restored Government of Virginia. Following considerable debate and countless meetings, the petition for a new state was presented to Congress on May 29, 1862. Upon approval of the petition, President Lincoln signed the related bill and on June 20, 1863, West Virginia became a state. The Cheat Mountain wolf pack now lived in West Virginia, not Virginia.

❧ *CHAPTER NINETEEN* ❧
THE LAST ELK

The Civil War and the reconstruction period during its aftermath coincided with the demise of elk in the central Appalachians. Wolves on Cheat Mountain had killed numerous elk during the late 1700s, but not enough to cause a decline in the overall population. As a result of taking primarily young and less fit older individuals only the excess animals were removed. The elk population had remained relatively stable from year to year, as elk and wolves coexisted in a balanced ecosystem.

Wolves seldom attacked a healthy adult elk, because of risk of personal injury. Settlers, however, were inclined to kill the largest, and in most cases, the healthiest individuals. The larger the elk, the better the target it provided for a rifle. And of course the larger the antlers the more impressive the trophy the hunter could hang on his cabin wall.

Elk had been relatively abundant around Cheat Mountain during the late 1700s, but by 1850 they were rarely seen by settlers or wolves. Three elk were killed by settlers along the Black Fork of the Cheat River in 1843, seven were seen along the Greenbrier River near Bartow in 1847, and one was reported in Canaan Valley in the 1860s. The last known death of an elk from human hunters in West Virginia occurred in 1867 at Elk Lick in Pocahontas County, along the eastern edge of the Cheat Mountains. In 1873, hunters discovered elk tracks near the headwaters of the Shavers Fork River, but no other sightings of tracks or animals were reported in West Virginia after that date.

The tracks discovered in 1873 were possibly made by the same animal the Cheat Mountain wolf pack pursued in late winter 1874. "Okanid", the alpha male, and his pack were at the southern extremity of their hunting range when they detected the animal's scent. The adult bull had wandered into the small valley along the upper reaches of the Tygart River the previous day. He had spent most of the winter in the Greenbrier River watershed east of Cheat Mountain in Pocahontas County. Although Okanid and the alpha female had encountered elk when they were youngsters, no other wolf in the Cheat Mountain pack had ever seen one.

Okanid sounded the stalk yip and all six wolves swung behind him as he altered his direction of travel and headed slightly downwind of the elk. The cautious stalk required nearly 32 minutes before Okanid guided the wolves into view of the elk. Weighing nearly 600 pounds, the bull supported a huge set of antlers consisting of four points on one side and five on the other. He was pawing through the foot-deep snow to reach dried grasses when his peripheral vision detected movement nearly 60 yards away. He abruptly raised his head, studied the predators for less than 30 seconds in the dim moonlight, and erupted into flight. In 20 seconds he was running full speed and the wolves initiated their attack.

A thin crust enabled the wolves to skim across the snow surface, whereas the elk broke through with each step. Had the snow been deeper the elk would have been at a major disadvantage, but one foot of snow was not a serious impediment. The wolf pack galloped silently in pursuit, gaining on their intended prey with each leap. The quiet of the night was broken by the muffled thud of hooves. Small clouds of condensed air puffed from the bull's nostrils as its hooves kicked up spraying snow. When the distance closed to 20 yards, the wolves moved to a wide attack front. At ten yards the final charge seemed imminent.

Immediately ahead was the Tygart River. Although only 20 feet wide and 1 foot deep, the stream provided an excellent spot for the bull to make a stand. Stopping in mid-stream, the elk turned to face his pursuers. The bull had learned that wolves would typically not attack if their prey held its ground. Most wolves needed the stimulus of running prey to press the attack. A yearling wolf made the first leap, but was caught in mid-air by the massive antlers. The bull was eight years old and in his prime. He had both experience and strength and had survived attacks by other wolves and even a yearling mountain lion.

The wolf pack surrounded the elk, but the water hindered their efforts. They attempted several ineffective leaps at the bull. Okanid did manage to rip a deep gash in the bull's left hip, but the injury did not limit its defense. Unable to gain solid footing from which they could launch an attack, four of the wolves retreated to the stream bank where they sat silently and studied their intended victim.

After a few minutes of rest, each of the observers on the bank plunged into the water with renewed vigor, but with the same results. One young female was struck by a powerful hind hoof and a juvenile male had his shoulder pierced by an antler point. Within 20 minutes, Okanid realized the risk exceeded the reward with this particular elk and yipped the signal calling an end to the hunt. The wolf pack moved silently into the foothills and resumed their search for more vulnerable prey.

Elk soon joined buffalo on the list of wildlife eradicated from the Allegheny Mountains. The hunter cannot survive without the hunted. When the hunted is no longer available, the hunter will slowly perish. Never again did wolves enjoy the thrill of stalking and attacking an elk in the Allegheny Mountains. One more component of the mountain ecosystem had been eliminated.

By 1875, only two packs of timber wolves inhabited Cheat Mountain, compared to over 15 in the early 1700s. Okanid and his pack of six wolves lived at the southern end and the second pack, consisting of only five individuals, lived at the northern end. As prey animals had declined during the early 1800s, the size of each pack's territory expanded. Whereas the territory size of Lupa's pack in the mid-1750s had been 50 square miles, that of Okanid's pack encompassed more than 400 square miles. With a scarcity of deer, Okanid's pack spent nearly twice as many hours hunting each night as Lupa's pack. Time available for socializing was greatly reduced.

Numbers of deer, elk, and bison were considerably lower in 1875 than they had been in the early 1700s, but the total number of large hoofed animals was nearly the same—especially in the Tygart Valley. Lands that once supported large herds of deer and elk now supported numerous herds of cattle. Wolves had largely ignored the domestic cattle during the 1700s, but as natural prey declined they became more and more drawn to the new hoofed animals. By 1800, wolves were killing several dozen cattle each year throughout Tygart Valley. Settlers could not put all their cattle in barns each night and split-rail fences did little to deter a hungry wolf. To complicate matters, each summer a few settlers moved their beef cattle to high mountain meadows. Herdsmen and their hounds guarded each herd during daylight hours, but they were relatively ineffective at night.

Okanid avoided the areas carrying the "scent marking" of humans, but when the pack went three or four days without killing a deer, hunger overcame his caution. Calves and yearling cattle were easy prey to bring down, easier than full-grown deer. Full-grown cattle were much more of a challenge. However, Okanid developed a technique that became highly effective as it was perfected.

While the pack had been attacking a half-grown steer of nearly 600 pounds, Okanid twice failed to clamp his jaws onto the steer's hindquarters. But on the third leap he accidentally grabbed the animal's tail. Instinctively holding tight, he was swung behind the steer. In a few seconds, the momentum of his body and a sudden jerk of his head pulled the steer off balance and it tumbled awkwardly to the ground. Instantly, four other wolves clamped their jaws onto the animal and escape was impossible. The wolves ate well that night and the two that followed.

In two months Okanid learned to target the tails of fleeing cattle, and a new hunting skill was learned. Occasionally, Okanid's sharp premolars severed the tailbone and the cow escaped the attack—although it lost much of its tail. In three months the skill was perfected—and gradually learned by other wolves. The pack began hunting beef cattle regularly and Okanid led the hunting party to mountain meadows and valley pastures instead of to habitats frequented by white-tailed deer.

Settlers and farmers bought more hounds, purchased steel leg-hold traps, and declared war on the few remaining wolves. The wolf bounty was raised to $40 by the Randolph County Commission and a few professional wolf hunters moved into the area. The pack that roamed the northern end of Cheat Mountain was the primary target of hunters because it was closer to Elkins and Beverly. Within five years that pack had been eliminated. Now only Okanid's pack remained.

Okanid, himself, had previously escaped capture when a steel trap clamped tightly on the middle toe of his right-front foot. Escape occurred only when a violent jerk of the foot painfully severed the toe. From that day on, he avoided every trap set on a trail or near a carcass. Although he became super cautious and learned to associate human scent with steel traps, young wolves in his pack were not so careful. Okanid's pack lost two members to steel traps. The first to be captured was a six-month old female. Barely a month later, a yearling male was unable to resist the powerful scent attractant placed on a tree stump at the edge of a trail along the Shavers Fork River.

Late winter of 1885, Okanid led the dwindling pack along the Shavers Fork River in search of a meal. The four-member pack often went three or four days without eating. They had killed a calf along the Elkwater Fork of Tygart River three weeks earlier, but had not filled their stomachs since that meal. The owner of the calf, an experienced hunter, had set off in pursuit the day after the calf carcass was discovered. He went alone, believing he had an excellent chance of stalking close enough to surprise the wolves. The wolf tracks led him across the iced-over Tygart River, along the foothills, and up onto Cheat Mountain where deep snows made travel difficult. After two days, he finally caught sight of the wolves, but was not close enough to get a good shot. As shadows began to lengthen, the wolves trotted into a clearing nearly 200 yards distant. The hunter leaned his Springfield rifle against a spruce tree, took careful aim, and slowly squeezed the trigger.

The wolf pack had been chased by hounds three times that month, and had been shot at several times. An earlier bullet had grazed Okanid's shoulder. At the sound of the rifle, Okanid exploded into action. The bullet kicked up a small clump of snow behind him. Before the hunter could get off another shot the wolf pack was out of sight. Too weary to continue, the hunter abandoned pursuit.

Okanid kept his pack on Cheat Mountain in the ensuing weeks, reluctant to risk another hunting excursion into the valley where hunters, hounds, and rifles awaited. On this particular spring day, Shavers Fork was running high. Warm weather had broken the hold of winter and huge chunks of ice inched slowly downstream. The pack had hunted along the river for nearly two miles, weaving through stands of spruce and hardwoods. Okanid spotted a small flock of wild turkey scratching under a stand of black cherry trees on the opposite side of the river.

The glossy black birds were searching for the pits of wild black cherries that remained from the previous fall's crop. Although the fleshy portion of the fruit had decomposed, the pit contained gratifying nourishment for the large birds. Little food remained on the forest floor for turkeys, and every acorn, beechnut, chestnut, spruce seed, and cherry pit was hungrily swallowed. The bird's gizzard would crush and grind the "hard mast" before it was moved into the stomach for digestion. Long, powerful legs and an efficient digestive system allowed these majestic birds to survive under conditions where few other birds could.

Alerting his pack, Okanid cautiously led the wolves to the river's edge. Turkeys had even better eyesight than wolves, and Okanid knew he had little chance of stalking close enough to capture one of the birds. However, hunger drove him to try. Wild turkeys had been abundant throughout Cheat Mountain in the early 1800s, but hunting by humans and loss of habitat had reduced their numbers drastically. Only a few flocks remained after the Civil War. The wary birds could escape most predators by flying up into a tree, but the highly accurate Springfield rifles and ten-gauge shotguns made the birds vulnerable to hunters.

Warming daytime temperatures and lengthening daylight hours had triggered the onset of breeding season for the wild turkeys along Shavers Fork. Eschewing caution, one mature gobbler was strutting before the hens, attempting to convince them he was the most impressive turkey in the woods. With spread tail feathers, puffed-out breast, and brightly-colored head and neck, he did indeed present an imposing sight. The performing gobbler appeared nearly twice the size of other birds in the flock and made an enticing target for the hungry, male wolf.

Okanid located a spot some 60 yards upstream of the turkeys where timber grew close to the riverbank, and a large birch tree hung out over the ice. Floodwaters had washed away its roots and it hung precariously low. Crouching with chest brushing the snow, Okanid cautiously stepped onto the ice and began his stalk. Normally the wolf would not have attempted such a risky maneuver, but hunger will drive any animal to extreme behaviors. Okanid was somewhat hidden by the leaning birch, and he progressed nearly half way across the river without being spotted by his prey. The middle of the river was a jumbled mass of large ice blocks that drifted slowly with the waters of Shavers Fork. Okanid studied each ice block carefully before taking his next step. Many blocks were seven feet wide and provided solid footing. Others were only one foot wide however. Suddenly, a block shifted as the alpha male stepped on its edge and Okanid's claws dug shallow grooves in the ice before his front foot slipped into the water.

Trembling nervously, Okanid regained his footing. He looked back over his shoulder at his waiting pack then searched anxiously for the turkeys. They were still feeding, unaware of the wolf that was nearly half way across the river. Blocks of ice in front of him were grinding together as they shifted position and subsequently created foot-wide sections of open water. Okanid tensed in anticipation of jumping to the next block, then smoothly vaulted over the open water. Unfortunately, his front feet slipped upon impact, the ice block shifted, and Okanid was plunged into the icy river. He was drawn under the ice block by the moving water, but his head re-emerged on the other side. The wolves stared intently, waiting for their leader to reappear. But Okanid was trapped amidst the colliding ice and would never again lead his pack in pursuit of wild turkeys or a farmer's calf. The Cheat Mountain wolf pack had lost another leader.

⚬ *CHAPTER TWENTY* ⚬
ONE SMALL PACK

By 1891, the Cheat Mountain pack, the last surviving timber wolf pack in West Virginia and the entire Appalachians, consisted of only four individuals: "Silva", the alpha male, "Aestiva", the alpha female, and two of the alpha female's pups, "Montani" and "Luesta". The two older wolves had learned from experience to avoid humans and their traps. They passed that knowledge on to the pups, which at a young age had become wary of human scent.

During the summer of 1891, Silva led his pack to the headwaters of Shavers Fork River. They avoided humans and even those cattle bearing a trace of human scent. An occasional deer supplemented a diet of groundhogs, beaver, turkey, rabbits, and rodents. Berries and fruits were consumed to compensate for a lack of meat. The wolves seldom hunted as a pack that summer. Stalking of a groundhog by a single wolf was more successful than four wolves attempting to stalk and pounce on the same target. One stalker was less likely to be detected than four stalkers.

Snows were heavy that winter and drifts exceeded eight feet by January. Groundhogs were hibernating and beaver seldom left the security of a den and its associated pond. Rodents concentrated their activities below the snows and were thus sheltered well beneath the wolves.

Only a few hares, rabbits, and squirrels, plus grouse and turkey were active and provided potential prey. However, these did not provide enough food to satisfy the requirements of the four wolves. As a result, one night in mid-January, Silva led Aestiva, Montani, and Luesta off the mountain into the upper reaches of Elk River.

Farming that required extensive plowing had not proved profitable in the mountains. However, the mountain and valley pastures offered opportunities for grazing livestock, especially sheep. The earliest settlers had brought a few sheep along with their cattle and hogs. All three forms of livestock provided meat, but sheep provided something more—wool. Meat was essential, but wool was nearly as prized. An animal had to be killed to obtain its meat, but a sheep could be sheared annually for as long as it lived. And of greater gain, every year the ewes would produce lambs, which provided highly desirable mutton.

Sheep numbers had gradually increased throughout the Appalachians, especially following the Civil War. In West Virginia, the number of sheep increased from 452,000 in 1860 to over 785,000 in 1890. Numbers in Randolph County increased from 7,560 in 1860 to nearly 18,000 in 1890. Markets were developing and the sheep industry was expanding. Sheep, especially Merinos and Dorsets, were grazing those high mountain meadows and valley grasslands that had once supported herds of deer, elk, and buffalo. Many farmers were dependent on their sheep for making a living. Merino sheep were great wool producers, and their fleeces contained the softest and finest of all wools. Such wondrous soft fleeces were one of the few cash crops available to Randolph County farmers.

The four wolves detected the smoke swirling from chimneys of two farmhouses, and made a wide detour to avoid them. An hour later, however, at the upper end of a large pasture, Silva detected the faint scent of fresh meat. The wolves were nearly 400 yards upwind of another cabin and did not detect human odor or smoke. Those scents would have prompted Silva to lead them away, just as he had earlier that night for the other two farmhouses. Cautiously approaching the scent, Silva got within ten yards before stopping and sitting on his haunches in the snow. A short distance away, lay the scattered remains of a dead sheep.

John Gregory, a local farmer had been feeding his Merinos from hay stored in the mow of a large log barn located 300 yards from his cabin. Daily he would trudge to the barn and throw out dozens of small piles of hay with his pitchfork. In spots, the snow was only a few inches deep and sheep could paw through for dried grasses. One yearling ram, more adventuresome than the others, wandered daily throughout the large pasture in search of sites where the sun had thawed the snow. A small stream trickled through the upper end of the pasture and provided drinking water to the sheep. Willow and viburnum bushes bordered one short segment of the stream.

The young ram had been attacked and killed by a hungry bobcat the previous night. The feline had eaten its fill and withdrew to a dense rhododendron thicket halfway up the mountain. Ravens alerted Gregory to the kill the next morning, and the farmer carved five, fist-sized chunks of meat from the carcass and carried them back to his cabin. Gregory had tried to trap marauding bobcats on several occasions, but had never been successful. In desperation, he had sent away for a small bottle of strychnine. Other farmers had sworn the poison would kill the wariest of predators.

Wearing gloves, Gregory made one deep cut into each of the chunks of sheep meat and carefully poured in a few grains of strychnine. Returning to the ram carcass that same morning he carefully tossed the chunks of meat beyond the remains, as far from his own tracks as possible. He had not touched the meat with bare hands and felt confident there would be little residual human scent by nightfall.

A bright sun that afternoon had slightly melted the snow and by darkness no human scent remained. Silva detected the strong odor of sheep emanating from the pasture and the barn where most now slept. The scene was similar to others where he had suspected steel traps and thus he cautiously circled the sheep carcass. No scent of humans, steel, or strange urine baits was detected. Only the faint scent of the bobcat permeated the cold night air. Still warning his three companions to stay away, Silva moved slowly towards the chunks of mutton a short distance from the carcass. He hungrily sniffed the first, but instinctively resisted the sweet smell of raw red meat. Likewise he resisted the second chunk. But at the third he carefully licked off a dried drop of blood. In so doing, the wolf detected a slight hint of human scent. He cautiously moved toward the sheep carcass and examined it suspiciously. Silva tore off a small piece of mutton and chewed it slowly.

Upon seeing Silva eat, the alpha female lost some of her fear. She and her two pups approached the carcass, but the hungry alpha male bared his teeth, snarled viciously, and drove them away. As they retreated, Aestiva discovered the poison-laden chunks. In less than ten seconds she ravenously gulped down three of the pieces so carefully tossed by Gregory. The female pup consumed the other two.

Within five minutes, Aestiva and Luesta began to slobber uncontrollably and thrashed wildly. In another five minutes the alpha female and her pup exhibited death throes and their lives came to an agonizing end. Silva and Montani sniffed around the bodies before fleeing the scene. The slobber from Aestiva's mouth dried on some grass and was licked by a fox that night. The fox remained near the sheep, and consumed a large portion of the meat. Aestiva's and Luesta's bodies were discovered by ravens soon after daylight arrived and they pecked out their eyes and tongues. Gregory discovered two dead wolves, a dead fox, and three dead ravens around the sheep carcass when he visited it that afternoon.

ᧁ *CHAPTER TWENTY-ONE* ᧁ
RABIES

Silva and Montani roamed the mountainsides throughout Randolph County for the next month, during which time they eluded hunters, hounds, traps, and strychnine. Montani, the male pup, followed the alpha male as he had followed his mother before her death. However, in late February Silva began to wander widely, running many miles with no apparent goal. At times when Montani was napping during mid-day, Silva would quietly rise to his feet and slip away into the nearby forest. Usually he came back later that day, or Montani was able to follow his scent and eventually locate him.

Late one afternoon Montani awoke and again found Silva missing. This time he failed to find the adult wolf and hunted by himself that night. For the first time in his life he was truly alone.

Silva was an adult male, and February marked the beginning of breeding season for wolves. The urge to breed directed his every action, even overpowering the urge to eat on some days as he hunted the scent of a mate.

One sunny afternoon in late February, the solitary timber wolf sat upright on his haunches, atop one of the many sandstone boulders that fringed the mountain rim overlooking Becky's Creek. Blue jays scolded and ravens emitted their rusty-hinge call. With trees now leafless, large objects moving across the snow-covered valley floor were easily visible.

Silva had sired four litters of pups but now had no female partner. His first sightings of some large canines evoked pleasant memories, until he realized they were not wolves. Wolves are social animals, needing constant companionship. Their lives are most rewarding when they run as a pack, sleep together in the warm sun, and howl as a cohesive unit because life is good. Silva longed for this, listening in vain on moonlit nights for the inviting call of another of his kind. But his intense concentration was never rewarded.

One night in March he detected the faint odor of a female hound in heat. His deep longing for a companion tugged so strongly that he slipped off the mountain, moved downwind of the cabin, and stealthily approached to within 300 yards. His sense of smell distinguished the sweet odors of livestock and the alluring odors of hounds, but intermixed were the dreaded odors of humans. Whatever attraction there might have been to the female hound was outweighed by the repulsive human odors.

Silva remained on Becky's Creek for an hour that night, as he analyzed the human odors drifting downwind with the evening breeze. A smoky blue haze, which emanated from the numerous houses, hung over the valley floor and compromised Silva's sense of smell. Dejected, and frightened, he turned northward and began his hunt. Wolves have deeply ingrained memories of the past, even drawing on learning experiences of earlier generations, but they have no cognizance of the future. They associate pursuit of prey with a warm, satisfying meal, but they do not contemplate the events of the next day. Silva had no way of knowing there were no female wolves left.

Two nights later, Silva returned and again closely observed the hounds. The urge to socialize was so strong he pointed his nose to the sky, opened his mouth, and howled. Twice, and then a third time he repeated the howl. One of the hounds chained to the porch responded with a howl—not a real howl, but a semblance of one retrieved from its ancestral past.

As barred owls began to call, Silva slipped off the rocky promontory and began a cautious descent towards the cabin. Gliding silently through a hardwood stand, the wolf was within 200 yards of the cabin when he spotted movement at the base of a large white oak. Ever alert for a meal, he began a tree-to-tree stalk, which brought him within five yards of his target. The animal's odor revealed its identity—a raccoon. Patiently, Silva waited while the raccoon scratched through the leaves around the white oak in search of last year's acorns. But when the raccoon began to climb the tree Silva took three quick steps and initiated the leap that would provide a much-needed meal.

The raccoon was nearly five feet off the ground when Silva made contact. The raccoon was a full-grown male, weighing nearly 20 pounds. As Silva tightened his grip, the raccoon twisted sideways and nipped at Silva's right front foot. It was not a serious bite, but did penetrate the skin. Normally, this bite would have been of no consequence to Silva, but this situation was different—drastically different. Foamy saliva covered the raccoon's jaws and teeth and it inflicted another bite to Silva's leg before dying. The raccoon had rabies!

This dreaded disease first appeared in England in 1734 and was reported in Virginia in 1753. Large numbers of red foxes were imported from England for red-coated horsemen who treasured the sport of fox chasing. Rabies outbreaks occurred in Boston and other New England towns during 1768-1771. By 1785 canine rabies was common across North America, spread by dogs, foxes, and wolves. Farm animals and other wild carnivores, including raccoons, carried the disease in Virginia and West Virginia during the 1800s.

Silva ate the raccoon that night and retreated back onto the mountain. In days, having descended into the rabid stage, Silva attacked a Jersey milk cow, a free-running hound, and a large red fox. Driven mad, three weeks later Silva was dead, one of hundreds of Cheat Mountain wolves that succumbed to rabies-induced seizures and paralysis during the 1800s.

EDWIN DARYL MICHAEL

❧ *CHAPTER TWENTY-TWO* ❧
SNOWSHOE HARE

Montani, the surviving male pup, spent most of March and April in the high mountain meadows between Elk River and Shavers Fork River. He became adept at capturing enough rabbits, rodents, grouse, and turkey to satisfy his hunger and his body weight stabilized at a healthy 60 pounds. Rarely did he encounter a deer, and when he did he made no effort to attack. He realized the risks associated with attacking an animal twice his weight.

Montani did not know he was the only wolf living on Cheat Mountain, and it would not have affected his life had he known. Montani was a unique individual. He had been super-curious from birth and learned faster than any of his siblings. He had constantly observed and mimicked the adults and by six months of age had become skilled at detecting human scent and the associated hidden traps. Although not large, he was more coordinated and quicker in movement than either of his parents. His deep chest and shallow mid-section accommodated economical movement, enabling him to cover over 100 miles in a day.

Much of Montani's first summer alone and the following autumn were spent in and around the open areas atop Cheat Mountain. Humans rarely ventured into these remote areas, and small prey animals were abundant. The boggy sites offered little for humans, except a few blueberries.

On the wind-swept plateaus lived an animal that changed color as the days shortened each autumn, becoming white to blend in with the snow that blanketed the landscape. The transformation from brown to white, and conversely from white to brown the subsequent spring, enabled the animal to escape detection. This unusual animal was the snowshoe hare, so named because of its huge furry hind feet that support the animal in deep snow and greatly improve its chances of outmaneuvering ground predators. It was also called "varying hare" because of its trait of changing coat color to match its surroundings.

The high mountain plateau was nearly ideal habitat for snowshoe hares, and during the late 1800s their population numbered in the thousands. The 4,000-foot elevation guaranteed that snow cover would persist from November through March, and would provide a background that made hares nearly invisible to passing predators.

Snowshoe hares rarely live to be more than two years old. However, living on Cheat Mountain in 1892 was one hare that had attained the extraordinary age of nine years. This female *Lepus americanus*, as scientists refer to the snowshoe hare, had reached old age through a combination of exceptional survival skills and remarkable good fortune.

The wilderness was characterized by daily, never-ending conflict. Settlers introduced another set of conflicts, those involving their hunting and trapping. Whereas hunting occurred year-round, trapping for valuable furs and pelts was a winter activity, when temperatures were low, snow covered the ground and pelts were thick.

The Hamrick boys who lived in the Elk River watershed trapped the mountains above their cabin every winter. One line of snares set by the Hamricks crossed the home range of "Lepus", the nine-year old snowshoe hare. Wire snares were strategically set in trails created by hares during their nocturnal feeding forays. A loop of wire, four to five inches in diameter, was suspended across the trail at the height of a hare's head. The animal's head, but not its shoulders, would pass through the circle. When the animal attempted to escape, the wire loop would tighten around its neck.

Montani had never encountered a wire snare and was unaware of the danger one presented. The opening of a snare set for a hare was only four to five inches wide, too small for a wolf's head to enter. However, a wolf running full-speed along a trail, with mouth wide open and nose to the trail, could thrust its snout deep into a deadly snare. Or more likely, its upper jaw would enter the snare, resulting in the wire being snagged behind molars or premolars. Struggling could force the wire deep into the flesh and injury, if not death, could occur.

Lepus had narrowly escaped capture in a snare the previous winter, and from then on the hare adroitly avoided each snare she encountered, several of which held dead snowshoes. However, one night in December her caution was diverted by the surprise attack of Montani. The moon had been hidden behind thick, fast-moving clouds all night, and the large doe (a female hare) felt secure in the safety of darkness as she searched for tender twigs.

Suddenly the clouds parted and the three-quarter moon threw the full power of its soft, silver rays across the plateau. Lepus knew to be extra alert when the moon was full or nearly so, but on this cloudy night she had ventured over 30 yards from the nearest dense cover. Slowly, but cautiously, Lepus moved towards the safety of a small stand of red spruce. Unbeknownst to the hare, Montani stood alertly upon a pile of large boulders only ten yards downwind. The wolf did not spot Lepus directly, but quickly associated its moving shadow with a meal.

Silently dropping from the boulders, Montani stalked through a clump of blueberry bushes to within striking distance. Jumping through the frigid air, the wolf landed in the well-worn trail, only 15 feet behind the hare. The hare, which could run 35 miles per hour and leap ten feet in a bound, hurled her five-pound body down the trail.

The previous day the Hamrick brothers had set a snare in the trail at the edge of the same red spruce stand an unsuspecting Lepus now so frantically sought. With a pursuing predator only ten feet behind, the hare rushed headlong down the trail directly towards the snare. If the hare somehow eluded the snare, the wolf could be the victim. The Hamrick boys would find an ensnared wolf rather than a strangled hare. A wolf pelt was many times more valuable than a hare pelt, plus its scalp would bring bounty money from the Sheriff.

In her panic to escape the wolf, it was Lepus that ran into the loop, and was immediately brought to a halt. Montani was surprised by the actions of the tumbling, kicking, choking hare, but did not delay his attack. The claws on the hind feet of an adult snowshoe hare offered limited defense, but they were nearly worthless against wolves. In a matter of seconds the hare breathed her last and life drained from the blood-splattered prey. Her flesh would extend Montani's survival several days closer to springtime and the more plentiful food supply it brought.

❧ *CHAPTER TWENTY-THREE* ❧
LONE WOLF

Montani wandered widely during the winter of 1892-1893, and in March some unknown force pulled the yearling wolf north, in the direction of the den where he had been born and where he had spent his first summer. He moved over Swecker Ridge and across Stewart Run, following the base of foothills forming the eastern boundary of Tygart Valley. Where he was going he did not know, although he had a pressing desire for companionship. He harbored vague reflections of other wolves, of howling and licking and muzzling. But he had never run with a large pack, had never participated in the attack of a full-grown elk or a full-grown white-tailed buck.

Spring was a time of abundance for most wildlife. Young animals born that year had not yet learned to avoid predators and such prey were readily available to Montani. Rodents, rabbits, birds, and an occasional deer fawn provided ready nourishment for the wolf. Bear cubs provided a rare meal, although mother bears seldom became separated from their cubs and easily defended them against a single wolf.

Foraging for meadow voles, however, supplied the most protein. The meadows, grassy balds, and bogs atop Cheat Mountain were optimal habitat for the voles and hunting conditions were superb for predators. Montani had considerable competition from hawks, owls, weasels, foxes, bobcats, and snakes. However, he had learned the stalk and pounce skills the previous year, and by July had perfected them to the extent that he was more successful than any other predator on Cheat Mountain. A rodent diet was supplemented with salamanders, snakes, fish, and bird eggs. The discovery of a grouse or turkey nest provided a special treat as the dozen or so eggs were hastily devoured.

On one occasion, as he was searching for meadow voles in the tall grasses bordering a beaver pond, Montani discovered the nest of a mallard and noted that all bird's eggs taste basically the same. Unfortunately for the wolf, nesting waterfowl were scarce on Cheat Mountain and provided little nourishment. Mallards and black ducks nested in the grasses and wood ducks nested in hollow trees, but no other ducks were present. Geese passed overhead during their spring and autumn migrations, but rarely landed.

By October Montani had honed the skills required for solitary hunting. Pack strategies involving leadership of an alpha male and cooperation of all individuals were of no value. He stalked and outran snowshoe hares, which rarely sought the asylum of an underground den. He diligently searched for groundhog burrows, then selected a strategic spot from which he could patiently observe the burrow opening. He learned to judge the critical distance at which a groundhog was too far from the burrow to reach it safely when a surprise attack occurred.

Montani learned to patiently pursue a flock of turkeys until they went to roost, then wait in ambush and intercept an unwary individual as it flew down from the treetop the following morning. He learned that muskrats were most vulnerable when in their bank dens along the borders of beaver ponds, sites where they could be dug out.

Montani became intimately familiar with travel routes used by deer and turkey when they visited chestnut and white oak stands. He knew every salt lick and watering hole where deer came daily to drink and waited patiently along narrow draws where his prey had reduced opportunities for escape. He spent hours reclined on vantage points around bogs and beaver ponds, and observed paths used by deer as they came in search of succulent aquatic plants. Such knowledge put prey at a major disadvantage and swung the odds in Montani's favor.

While waiting along a deer trail or on an open hillside the lone wolf searched the skies for vultures and ravens. The distinctive swoosh, swoosh, swoosh created by a flying raven passing close overhead was never ignored. Concentrations of these scavengers caught his attention and often prompted an investigation of the site where the large black birds were circling.

One former food that had previously provided a tasty treat for wolf packs was not available to Montani. That was the sweet flesh of passenger pigeons. Had the flocks still darkened the sky as in the 1700s, Montani could have feasted nightly on those young squabs that tumbled from their nests. Unfortunately, the passenger pigeons that numbered in the millions no longer nested in the Cheat Mountains. Relentless market hunting had decimated most flocks and only small remnant groups visited the Cheat Mountains during the decade following the Civil War. A few pigeons migrated through West Virginia during the 1880s and 1890s, and the last communal nesting occurred in 1889. A group of several hundred pigeons attempted to nest near the headwaters of the Greenbrier River that spring, but they were not successful due to overzealous hunters.

Even plant foods supplemented Montani's diet. By June, serviceberries were dropping and by July the early-blooming blueberries were bearing ripe fruit. Morels, oyster mushrooms and large puffballs were cautiously consumed. Autumn made available other plant items—foods the members of a wolf pack would rarely eat. Montani consumed viburnum berries and grapes, white oak acorns and chestnuts, persimmons and pawpaws. The wolf typically obtained ten pounds of food each day and managed to steadily gain weight. By November he weighed 95 pounds. While not so large, nor as powerful as a mature male wolf, he had size and strength aplenty to kill the small prey that dominated his daily diet. Even full-grown beaver, weighing as much as 50 pounds, were easy prey.

Montani had attempted to dig through beaver dens in spring and early summer when kits were present, but usually failed. However, during fall when beaver were preoccupied with building food caches in the middle of their ponds Montani was at times successful. To obtain the trees used to form the caches, beaver ventured long distances from their ponds, often as much as 200 yards. After felling a tree, typically aspen, beaver would cut the tree into sections 2-3 feet long and haul them back to the pond. From there they anchored them in a single mass in the deepest part of the pond. Although the pond would freeze over in winter, a beaver could dive down out of its den, grasp a section of aspen tree, and pull it back into the den. After chewing the bark from the tree section the beaver would haul the smooth log back into the pond. There it would be added to the base of the dam to strengthen the already well-engineered structure.

During September and October, when beaver were actively cutting aspen, Montani would occasionally follow the edges of ponds and streams. The wolf would then follow the beaver scent until surprising the large rodent in the act of cutting a tree or hauling a log section. The large cutting incisors of a beaver were only a slight deterrent, and a highly nutritious meal was the outcome. With the demise of buffalo and elk, and the scarcity of white-tailed deer, no other animal provided the pounds of fatty flesh available from a beaver. Unfortunately, trapping had reduced beaver numbers by the 1880s, and only rarely did Montani locate an active beaver colony.

Montani looked like a timber wolf, but he certainly did not behave like one. He demonstrated neither the feeding behavior nor the social behavior that so identified a wolf. He had no mature alpha male to follow, no pack to interact with, no orchestrated chases and attacks of large hoofed animals, no wolf puppies to feed regurgitated foods, and no howling sessions to announce the initiation of a nightly hunt, a successful kill, or a proclamation to adjacent wolf packs. He certainly did not fulfill the complete definition of a timber wolf.

To those humans who occasionally saw his tracks, encountered his scat piles, or caught a glimpse of him, however, he was all wolf. He had the classic face, elongated muzzle and white cheeks with black lips that highlighted a characteristic grin. And always there existed the penetrating gaze highlighted with golden eyes—the eyes of death.

Montani was dark gray in color and sported an unusually dark bushy tail. But more importantly, he evoked in people all that his packs of ancestors had come to represent.

When the snows drifted deep on Cheat Mountain and Shavers Fork iced over, Montani once again moved into the foothills. Groundhogs had surrendered to hibernation, most songbirds had migrated to more friendly climates, and beaver were secure in their dens. By January, with small prey animals quite scarce, his behavior came to again reflect traits of a real timber wolf. Although he did not pursue deer, he did attack and kill an occasional sheep. The short, frigid days of winter produced hunger pangs, but the long nights provided many hours to investigate the sheep herds that were scattered around Tygart Valley.

Montani had abandoned his home territory and roamed, with no territorial limitations. Because there were no other wolf packs, he rarely scent-marked or followed established trails. Montani seemed driven to search for some unknown entity. He wandered constantly, seldom remaining in the same area for more than one day. When he killed a sheep he rarely returned for more than one meal. He had learned to associate sheep carcasses with humans and hounds and steel traps—and death. After killing a sheep he would move long distances, often as much as 30 miles in one night. Although sheep farmers set steel traps, scattered strychnine, and pursued him with hounds, they caught only foxes, bobcats, raccoons, and skunks. A rare mountain lion was even killed. Had his kills been more pronounced and regular on any one farm he would surely have attracted much more hunting pressure. But rarely did he revisit the same farm in one winter. Those farmers with dead sheep who failed to see his tracks argued strenuously that the kills were not the work of a wolf, but of some unknown beast.

❧ *CHAPTER TWENTY-FOUR* ❧
SAWMILLS AND SHEEP

Montani reached sexual maturity at two years of age, but he had never mated or courted a female. Nevertheless, the drive to mate instinctively appeared. He wandered widely, searching for that which did not exist.

There were wolves in northern Michigan, 500 miles away as well as in Canada. Such a journey was certainly possible, although the obstacles were nearly insurmountable, and Montani had no instincts to guide him. Montani's race was nearing its end if he remained in the central Appalachians. With one male and one female there is always hope. But with only one surviving animal there can be no hope. The end is constantly in sight, only a few heartbeats away.

Montani searched in vain responding to an instinct that drove him to search again for a female. He carefully sniffed every scat pile and every log and every rock along the miles of trails he covered. He encountered and recognized scent deposits left by female foxes and female mountain lions and female bobcats, and his curiosity was roused. But he knew instinctively the scent deposits were not made by the potential mate he so earnestly sought.

Montani left the Shavers Fork region in the summer of 1894. Never again would he roam the Becky's Creek watershed. Logging, on a commercial scale, had come to the region and the disturbance was intolerable to the wolf. Extensive logging had occurred near Cheat Bridge during the Civil War, but that lasted less than one year and forest quickly regenerated. Within ten years, saplings dominated much of the area where Cheat Summit Fort had been erected.

A small sawmill had been built near Valley Head in 1822, but that was moved and only one existed in Randolph County in 1835. That was near Mingo. Several water-powered sawmills were constructed throughout upper Tygart Valley during the Civil War. With no railroads to transport logs or lumber, such mills supplied only local needs. Following the Civil War several attempts were made to float logs down the Cheat River to sawmills at Rowlesburg.

The first large log drive was in 1880, when several thousand large poplar logs were floated down Shavers Fork. In 1884, another log drive was initiated. This would float thousands more logs down the Shavers Fork from the vicinity of Cheat Bridge to a large circular saw at Point Marion, Pennsylvania, a distance of 180 miles. The river was dammed to create temporary, log holding, splash ponds and dynamite was used to blast large boulders from the river. Countless logs became lodged against boulders, against the bank, or across other trapped logs, and never reached the sawmill. Consequently, these log floats were not considered successes.

Considerable logging occurred on Cheat Mountain during the early 1880s, following the great die-off of red spruce in the Shavers Fork area. The first major logging operation on Cheat Mountain began in 1888, when Colonel A.H. Winchester began cutting timber along the Shavers Fork River. Nearly 200,000 acres of virgin timber remained in Randolph County, principally along Cheat Mountain. Winchester, working with W.S. Dewing and Sons, built a narrow gauge railway powered by Shay locomotives, upstream from Cheat Bridge. Extending nearly three miles, this railway provided access to tens of thousands of red spruce trees, the most valuable tree in the mountains. Col. Winchester also built a large log house near Cheat Bridge and in June of 1888 began establishing a logging camp.

A large splash dam was built one-half mile below Cheat Bridge for the purpose of concentrating logs. The large quantities of water stored behind the dam facilitated the subsequent log floats, as a torrent of released water would rush downstream. During late winter and early spring, when the river was running high, the dam was opened and logs were floated from Shavers Fork to the mouth of the Cheat River at Point Marion, Pennsylvania. There, a large mill converted the logs into useful boards, which were then moved further downstream on the Monongahela River to a lumber-hungry Pittsburgh.

Logging and the subsequent habitat destruction along the Shavers Fork continued until 1896, but Montani had left the region by 1894. Great stands of red spruce no longer lined the river. In their place stood thousands of wide, lifeless stumps. No chatty fairy diddles spent countless hours harvesting spruce cones. No flying squirrels foraged through the duff for underground fungi. No ruffed grouse strutted atop downed logs. With trees no longer overhanging the river the waters warmed and brook trout suffered. There remained little to attract a hungry timber wolf.

Life in the central Appalachians was changing rapidly, for both wildlife and humans. Never again would it resemble the wilderness seen when explorers originally came to the area. Greater changes were occurring during the 1800s than any since the last ice age, when massive glaciers pushed and scraped to within a few hundred miles.

The winter of 1894 was especially cold, and Montani often went three or four days without eating. Hunger drove him down out of the mountains and on the night of January 20, 1895, he approached the farm of Jacob Hamrick on Point Mountain in Randolph County. Hamrick had purchased a flock of high-priced Dorset ewes the previous fall, with high hopes of developing a large herd. Wool was in high demand and would provide his family badly needed cash.

The wolf slipped through a split rail fence into a pasture holding the Dorsets. Rarely during his life had Montani killed more than he could consume. But on this night he was mysteriously drawn into a feeding frenzy. He easily killed one sheep, continued his attack, and soon killed a second and a third. Food had been scarce that winter, and sheep were so easy to kill—easier than any other animal. Montani continued to kill. Sheep were timid, weak, and fragile. They possessed no traits or physical features enabling them to survive a predator attack. They were perfect prey for a lone wolf. In less than 30 minutes, Montani had killed 27 sheep. Most of the Dorset ewes carried unborn lambs, many twins. By the time the slaughter had ended several crippled sheep lay around the pasture, all with large bloody wounds. This was the only mass kill Montani ever conducted. As was his usual pattern, he ate his fill from one of the sheep and then vacated the farm. The next night found him over 20 miles away. As a pup, Montani had loved to run and that love remained with him as an adult. Instinctively he was following the mantra of his ancestors; the wolf lives longest who runs fastest and farthest.

Montani continued to wander widely throughout southern Randolph County and also spent many months in Pocahontas and Webster counties. Although he concentrated on a variety of wild animals during summer months, he was forced to kill sheep during winter. Hundreds of steel traps were set and hundreds of hunts with hounds were conducted to put an end to the sheep killing. At the insistence of sheep farmers, the county courts of both Randolph and Webster counties offered incomparable bounties of $100 to the person who killed the marauding wolf. Farmers argued they were being driven out of business by the wolf, although free-ranging hounds were probably responsible for many of the sheep kills. In spite of the bounties, Montani remained alive because of skill, knowledge, and good fortune.

December of 1895 was extremely difficult for Montani. Food was scarce and he was forced to leave the mountains and hunt near homesteads. One extremely cold night, with the temperature near zero, Montani killed a young Dorsett ewe not far from the Elk River. The farmer, Lewis VanDevender, owned three large hounds, which he usually kept chained outside the barn. Because of the cold, they were sleeping inside the barn on that particular night. After eating his fill of the Dorsett ewe, Montani moved three miles before seeking shelter.

Upon discovering the sheep kill the next morning, VanDevender released his hounds on the wolf track. With rifle in hand, he took up the chase. At the first sound of hounds baying, Montani exited the spruce thicket where he had spent the night. Trotting effortlessly, the wolf moved towards the nearby mountains. The snow slowed VanDevender, and his hounds were soon nearly one-half mile ahead. By mid-day, VanDevender was so far behind his hounds he could barely hear their baying. Not wanting to spend the night away from his cabin, he blew his horn for the hounds to return, but they were too far ahead and failed to respond.

With the sun sinking low in the sky, Montani gained confidence. Although the hounds were coming closer, he did not break into a gallop. Instead he loped almost casually through the gloomy forest. As darkness overwhelmed the forest, Montani slowed.

For some reason, Montani felt agitated that particular December night, even combative. Carefully choosing a spot near a jumble of boulders, he stopped. Crouching low in the snow, with his rump to a boulder, he waited. The hounds neared and erupted in a chorus of barks and howls. VanDevender had progressed several hundred yards back towards his cabin when he caught the distant sounds of his excited hounds. If they caught up with the wolf and a fight ensued he would need to be present. He had paid good money for the trio and did not want to lose them. But his greatest incentive was the wolf bounty. He had matches and could light a torch if he located a suitable spruce knot.

The largest dog, a black and tan Virginia foxhound, stopped when he spotted Montani. Weighing nearly 70 pounds, he had killed numerous foxes, but quickly realized the wolf was larger than any animal he had fought. The second dog to arrive was smaller and younger. It possessed the long front legs, short black and white coat, and broad pendant ears that characterized many coonhounds. This young hound, which had been bred to hunt by scent and to tree raccoons, stopped beside the large hound and began barking incessantly. The third hound, weighing almost 60 pounds, was all black with brown feet. It had been bred from a Walker foxhound and was experienced at chasing foxes. The three hounds moved apart, with the large black and tan foxhound facing the wolf and the other two on opposite sides.

Montani tensed, and waited. He knew from experience that in this situation the attacker was at a disadvantage. The hounds yipped, barked, howled, and snarled, but Montani did not move. They rushed at their target, but still he did not move. Had Montani attempted to run, he would have been brought down. Growing impatient, the black Walker hound attacked. Attempting to grab the wolf's front leg, he leapt with wide-open jaws. Montani turned instinctively, slammed his shoulder into the attacker and as the black hound hit the ground Montani's jaws crushed upon his neck. Before the other two hounds could react, Montani gave a quick shake of his head and tossed the hound aside.

The other two hounds erupted in loud barks, but Montani resumed his defensive crouch. They snarled and feinted for over five minutes, before the young black and white coonhound sprung at Montani. The hound had killed several raccoons by clamping his jaws around their back, but that experience was of little value now. Still, it prompted overconfidence and thus put him at a great disadvantage. Crouched in the snow, with his rump pressed against the boulders, Montani's full size was not evident to the dogs. As the black and white hound rushed in, Montani almost casually shifted his position and clamped his jaws around the hound's left front leg. The bone broke, the hound howled in pain, and Montani released his grip. As the hound limped pitifully away from the fracas, Montani turned his full attention to the large black and tan foxhound. The hound growled menacingly, but did not attack. In the past when he had treed a coon or cornered a fox his owner had arrived shortly and brought an end to the animal's life with a rifle bullet. Realizing the fight now involved one-on-one, he dropped to the snow and began a steady barking.

VanDevender realized that only one hound was barking. Fearing the worst, he quickened his pace through the dark forest. The flickering flame from his spruce knot provided adequate light to avoid trees and boulders, but he was forced to move at a frustratingly slow pace. As long as the wolf was solidly bayed and remained in one spot, the farmer was confident of getting within rifle range.

Montani was confident he could kill the remaining hound if he chose to attack. But for some reason he remained stationary, with ears alert and eyes locked in a formidable stare. When the farmer was within 20 yards, his disturbing scent was carried directly to Montani. The wolf almost instantly steeled himself and erupted at the reddish brown hound. The large hound counter-attacked, and in so doing prevented Montani's jaws from clamping around his neck. Instead, four large canine teeth sliced open the hound's right shoulder. Fearing the approaching man, Montani rushed into the surrounding darkness and was 30 yards away before VanDevender reached his hounds. It became evident to the farmer that the hunt was over. One of his hounds was dead, one had a broken leg, and the third was bleeding badly from its shoulder.

EDWIN DARYL MICHAEL

CHAPTER TWENTY-FIVE
LAST HUNT

In the early morning hours of January 1, 1897, Montani visited the John Hamrick farm near Whitaker's Falls on the Elk River and killed five prize Merino sheep. Estimating his loss to be nearly $100 and concluding he could afford no more sheep kills that winter, Hamrick initiated a major hunt. He struggled through two feet of snow to the house of his brother Peter and pleaded for help. A wolf hunt was soon organized and every man who lived in the area was coaxed to join.

Stoffer Hamrick, the 17-year-old son of Peter Hamrick, was instructed to saddle his horse, ride to Joe Sharp's, and ask him to bring his hounds. Stoffer eventually reached the Sharp cabin and found him more than eager to help. By the time Stoffer Hamrick, Joe Sharp, and his eight hounds returned to the Hamrick house, John Hamrick and a neighbor had tracked Montani into a dense spruce thicket on Point Mountain, a short distance from the cabin of Currence Chapman. With darkness approaching, the two men decided to wait for more hunters, and more hounds.

Montani had moved into the spruce thicket after filling his stomach with mutton. He slept through the day until the voices of John Hamrick and his neighbor awoke him late that afternoon. As darkness wiped away all shadows, Montani abandoned the thicket and trotted nervously up the mountainside. Moving sporadically throughout the night, he was nearly six miles away before dawn. Believing the danger to have ended, Montani spent the day alongside a large chestnut tree that had fallen during a destructive ice storm the previous spring.

As word of the wolf hunt spread through the region, more and more hunters joined the group. By the time the hunting party formed halfway up Mill Run, there were 15 men and boys present. Those included Francis Cowger, John Doddrill, Garfield Doddrill, Lee H. Hamrick, Adam Hamrick, Calvin Hamrick, Spencer Hamrick, W. S. Hamrick, David W. Hamrick, Lilly Hamrick, Stoffer Hamrick, John Rose, Robert Rose, George Rose, and Joe Sharp.

The hunting party was a scruffy, rag-tag group, outfitted in a wide variety of clothing. All wore heavy leather boots and wool long johns. Most had wool socks, wool gloves or mittens, and wool or fur caps. Some had denim or leather overalls, while others wore heavy wool hunting pants. The majority wore one of several types of knee-length Mackintoshes sold by Sears Roebuck. A few wore long black oil slickers. Weapons varied even more than their clothing. One hunter had a new lever action repeating Winchester rifle. Others carried Sharps, Spencers, or Civil War Springfield rifles. Some were armed with 12-gauge single-barrel shotguns, loaded with black powder and buckshot.

Temperatures were below zero, and a thin icy crust covered nearly two feet of snow. By late afternoon Montani heard the distant barking of hounds. Enough wolf scent had persisted atop the snow that the hounds stayed in pursuit. Although they had lost Montani's scent in many places, eventually one of the eight hounds was able to discover a whiff of scent and they continued the chase. The dogs were a mix of foxhounds and coonhounds. Although none had ever chased a wolf, they were quite experienced in chasing foxes.

The hunting party made considerably less progress on the second full day. Montani and the hounds trotted smoothly on top of the crusty snow in most places, but the hunters broke through at nearly every exhausting step. Montani's tracks were easily followed for long stretches due to a light skift of newly fallen snow creating near perfect tracking conditions. Fortunately for the hunters, the wolf tracks were unlike any other they encountered, thus identification was not difficult. Measuring over five inches in length, with distinct claw marks, they were readily distinguished from those of mountain lions, which were slightly smaller and lacked the prominent claw marks.

As darkness fell, the hounds were enticed back to their hunters by the resonating notes blown from cow's horns and by the knowledge that food awaited. Both men and dogs were forced to rest all night and long periods of time during daylight hours because of exhaustion, but the hunt continued.

Montani moved in a huge circle through the dense forests as the persistent hunters followed. Never had Montani experienced such a relentless chase. While the hunters and their hounds had spent the previous night in a remote Hamrick mountain cabin, Montani slept atop the snow. His dense coat provided protection even at sub-zero temperatures. Especially valuable was his long bushy tail, which he used to cover his head while sleeping.

Of greater importance to the wolf than keeping warm was eating. But Montani had no food. He attempted to hunt while moving, but that was nearly impossible. Stalking required much patience, and food was scarce in the mountains at that time of the year.

Because no cabins or barns were available, the hunters and hounds spent that night around a campfire at the mouth of Flint Run on the Back Fork of the Elk. They had little food and several of the hunters were exhausted. A few hunters had abandoned the chase and a few others had taken their place. Several argued that they should abandon the hunt and resume when the weather improved. Others argued that this was their best chance to kill the wolf and it must be exhausted after three days of close pursuit. If they were ever going to rid their farms of this sheep killer, they must do it now.

While sitting around the campfire, Lilly Hamrick told Stoffer Hamrick, "I can't travel any more."

Jacob Hamrick suggested that someone go to his farm, get a horse, and bring it back for Lilly to ride. Stoffer and Lee Hamrick walked three miles through the deep snowdrifts on Point Mountain to Jacob's farm. However, while returning with the two horses, Stoffer and Lee met the hunting party with Lilly in the lead. Apparently, good-natured encouragement from his relatives and fear of being labeled a quitter had convinced Lilly to remain with the hunting party. Truth told; Lilly did not want to miss out on the kill of the last wolf in the Cheat Mountains.

The fourth day was relatively uneventful for the hunters, as they dragged themselves through knee-deep snow. They never caught sight of the wolf, which remained a few miles in front of its pursuers.

❧ *CHAPTER TWENTY-SIX* ❧
LAST MEAL

As dusk settled over the mountains, Montani tracked a small flock of wild turkeys but lost their scent at the point where they flew up into a large white oak to roost for the night. These remarkable birds spent even the coldest nights high up in trees, with their toes clamped firmly around tree limbs. Neither freezing temperatures nor driving winds forced them to roost at ground level.

Around midnight, the famished wolf discovered a large flying squirrel foraging beneath a red spruce stand. A slow stalk brought him tantalizingly close to the potential meal. However, the squirrel detected the wolf and scrambled safely to the lowest limb. Later that night Montani trailed a snowshoe hare through a rhododendron thicket, but again with no success.

As the first filtered light of dawn eased through the trees, Montani detected the faint scent of a ruffed grouse. These chicken-sized birds were year-round residents of the mountains. Grouse fed on a variety of foods in winter, including acorns, greenbriar berries, wild grapes, beechnuts, black cherry seeds, teaberries, and buds of various trees. They were well equipped for walking atop the snow, regardless of its depth, thanks to small projections on each toe forming a type of snowshoe.

Ruffed grouse in the central Appalachians survived below-zero nightly temperatures by snow roosting, a process where birds dove into the snow from high in a tree. The momentum of their dive would take them several feet under the snow. Obviously, soft snow was most preferred for such dives. Snow roosting protected grouse from the eyes of hungry barred owls. However, the birds were not so well protected from wolves.

Montani stalked ever closer to the source of the grouse scent, cautiously advancing one foot at a time. The wolf stopped three feet from the bird, crouched, and then leaped towards his target. Plunging into the soft snow with mouth wide open, Montani's jaws were poised to clamp onto any solid object they might encounter. Although the grouse was strategically positioned to erupt from the snow should danger threaten, it had failed to detect the approaching wolf. Too late it flushed from its snow den, and Montani's jaws closed over one wing. Under the snow the wolf quickly repositioned its jaws and in so doing clamped tightly around the grouse's body. Although the bird continued to flap, its life was ended.

Montani expertly pulled several mouthfuls of feathers from the tender white flesh of the breast and ravenously consumed the first meat he had eaten since killing the sheep five days previous. It took just four minutes to eat the entire bird, including feet, head, internal organs, and wings. Only a few feathers remained. But the grouse provided only two pounds of meat. To continue fleeing his pursuers, the wolf needed 10-15 pounds.

The following day the men discovered where Montani had killed the grouse and concluded they were not far behind. Their enthusiasm was rekindled. Plans were quickly made and hunters were assigned locations along the upper Elk River where they suspected the wolf could cross. A few hunters followed the wolf tracks with the hounds while the others waited eagerly at their shooting stands.

The hounds picked up Montani's scent and set off with renewed vigor. The wolf had been sleeping beneath a large hemlock when he heard the hounds baying. Quickly jumping to his feet, he galloped for nearly half a mile in a wide loop before slowing.

John Doddrill was leaning against a large tulip poplar when he caught sight of the wolf. At first he believed it to be one of their hounds. John had a new lever-action Winchester rifle and had only fired it three times. When the wolf came within 50 yards, he carefully leaned the rifle barrel against the side of the poplar, took dead aim at the wolf's shoulder, and pulled the trigger. Much to his shock, the gun did not fire. He tried again and again, as the wolf stood still, but the rifle still would not fire.

The movements by Doddrill, as he levered one more bullet into the chamber, were spotted by Montani, and he immediately burst into a wild gallop. No other hunter glimpsed the wolf and he eluded the ambush that had been set. With the baying hounds coming closer, Montani ran for two miles before slowing.

John Doddrill stayed at his hunting stand until the dogs and their handlers came into view. He called them and was soon detailing his experience. "Men, that wolf is not to be killed. I had it lined up perfectly in my sights at only 50 yards and my brand new rifle wouldn't fire."

Perplexed, they hunted in the snow and found two of the ejected cartridges that had failed to discharge. Doddrill inserted one into the chamber and pulled the trigger. It fired with a loud explosion of gunpowder. He chambered the second and it also fired. Doddrill pronounced, "The hand of the Almighty is against us. We cannot kill that wolf."

The other hunters tried to convince Doddrill that his rifle had misfired because of ice but he was not convinced. He replied, "I'll go with you, but don't place me where you think the wolf will come."

The hunting party made noticeably less progress on the sixth day than it had on the first few. Both men and dogs were forced to rest for long periods of time because of exhaustion. Tracking conditions had become difficult, and several times each hour they lost the wolf's trail. On such occasions, the men fanned out and moved in ever-larger circles, searching intently for sight of the distinct track. In late afternoon they found, and then lost the tracks again.

As darkness fell, they were forced to set up camp. They shared a few small pieces of dried beef and a handful of hard biscuits, but had nothing else to eat. Exhausted and thirsty, they curled beneath wool blankets around the large fire and attempted to sleep.

Upon waking the following morning, the seventh day, several men were ready to quit the chase. They were wet, cold, and hungry. However, Jacob Hamrick emphatically stated, "I lost 25 sheep to this killer and I won't quit until I see its blood staining the snow red."

The other men finally agreed to intensify the search for tracks, but agreed that if they had not found them by mid-day they would call off the hunt and return home. Three hounds had become so exhausted the hunters were forced to leave them at farmhouses. Dark storm clouds, portending an imminent snowstorm, drifted rapidly overhead.

Montani continued his trot, but was rapidly running out of stamina. Having eaten only the one grouse in six days, his body reserves had been depleted. Frequently he stopped for a rest and fell asleep for one or two hours, only to be awakened by the barking of hounds.

One large reddish hound led the chase during the entire hunt. When the scent was lost he was typically the one to relocate it. He ran at the front of the pack, and his loud bellowing howl was the first to reach Montani. The hounds had been fed several times during the chase and thus slowly gained an advantage over the harried wolf. Montani would normally have outrun the hounds, but an injured left foot slowed him. Two days earlier, he had stepped on a fallen limb from a hawthorn tree. A long sharp thorn had penetrated his footpad and broken off, leaving nearly an inch of thorn.

On the night of the seventh day, January 7, the men and their hounds were fed and sheltered by a Dutch family on Turkey Bone Mountain, in Randolph County. After a breakfast of grits, gravy, and biscuits, the hunting party moved to the spot where they had quit the night before—the head of Back Fork of Elk River.

Jacob Hamrick and Milton Hull remained behind to hold the dogs for an hour and a half before turning them lose on the wolf's trail. That would give the hunters time to reach their stands where they would await the wolf. The men spread out along the fork of the stream, each at a spot where he expected the wolf to cross. Most were standing alongside a tree trunk, while others were sitting behind a fallen tree. All were positioned so their silhouettes would not be noticed by an approaching wolf. The men were 50-100 yards apart, thus each hunter could see two or three others. Each held great expectations of shooting the wolf and collecting the bounty. The temperature was again near zero and after three hours Alva Sharp began to build a fire.

Montani had slept much of the previous night, but was nearing total exhaustion. If he could only find something to eat: a snowshoe hare or a crippled wild turkey, or even a meadow vole. How miraculous if he should discover the carcass of a dead deer, to gulp down mouthfuls of energy-giving meat. Ten pounds of venison would provide enough energy for him to run hours without stopping. If he eluded the hunters for another 24 hours they would likely abandon the chase.

The gaunt gray wolf swallowed large mouthfuls of snow to quench his ever-burning thirst, but he found nothing to eat. The sounds of the hounds once again reached the wolf's ears and once again he pushed wearily onward.

As Montani trotted slowly through the woods he caught a faint whiff of smoke from Alva Sharp's small fire. Instantly stopping, he attempted to locate the source of the smoke. However, the hounds were coming closer and it seemed likely he would be forced to defend himself against their attacks. Montani had been attacked on three previous occasions. Each time he had killed one of the dogs. He weighed more than any hound in the region and was a much more skilled fighter. If he could find a rhododendron thicket he would make his stand.

Montani was limping badly. The broken thorn had penetrated deeply and every step brought excruciating pain. With lungs burning, he began to pant heavily. He was more tired than ever in his life. Although muscles ached and burned, Montani did not give in to the agonizing fatigue. He was a wolf. In the face of likely defeat, dogs might tire and sulk whining back to their owners. But not a wolf!

Montani's heart was strong and on he limped. He began to search for a hole to enter, but because he was in strange country, he did not have the luxury of knowing every rock outcrop and every boulder field. He believed he could survive a battle with one dog or one pack. Most dogs were cowards, although a pack did gain confidence as the number of individual hounds increased. Many dogs would sit whining, fearful of this demonic beast—an animal so much like them, but so very different. Did they envy his strength and skills? Only a few thousand years ago they had been like him.

How easy it would be for Montani to stop, to curl up in the snow and await the hounds. A short rest would certainly refresh. He would regain the strength necessary to fight. Had he known he was the last wolf in the Appalachians, Montani might have tried even harder. Or, he might have conceded the cause was lost and concluded further flight was useless. Why not simply curl up in the snow and go to sleep? Why struggle to survive if you are the last of your species?

Montani changed his course of travel and consciously began moving towards the north. Unknowingly, his new direction carried Montani between Laben Hull and 17-year old Stoffer Hamrick. Stoffer was standing on a log that was lying against a large maple tree when he sighted the wolf. He quickly shouldered his rifle, exhaled his breath, steadied his grip, aligned the sights, and squeezed the trigger. Before Montani heard the sound of exploding black powder, the lead bullet slammed into him. Driven from his feet by the force, Montani sprawled awkwardly in the snow along the Elk River. His eyelids closed slowly and his left hind leg jerked spasmodically. Blood seeped from the bullet hole and death came quickly to the once majestic animal. There were wolves no more in eastern North America!

CHRONOLOGY OF MAJOR EVENTS

1753 – Robert Files and David Tygart first settlers in Tygart Valley.

1777 – Haddan's, Currence's, and Westfall's forts built in Tygart Valley.

1787 – Randolph County, Virginia created.

1787 – Bounties offered for dead wolves in Randolph County.

1800 – Population of Randolph County was 1,826.

1825 – Last known buffalo killed in Virginia/West Virginia.

1830 – Population of Randolph County was 5,000.

1848 – Staunton-to-Parkersburg Turnpike completed across Cheat Mountain.

1850 – Stagecoaches began running between Staunton, Virginia and Parkersburg, Virginia (later West Virginia).

1861 – Cheat Summit Fort (Fort Milroy) constructed near Cheat Bridge by Federal troops.

1867 – Last known elk killed in West Virginia.

1880 – Population of Randolph County was 8,102.

1881 – Major logging occurred along Shavers Fork River.

1889 – Last sighting of passenger pigeons in West Virginia.

1897 – Last known wolf killed in West Virginia – the last known timber wolf killed in the central Appalachians.

1897 –Stoffer Hamrick was paid a $100 bounty for a wolf scalp: the last bounty paid for a wolf in West Virginia.

1941 –The *Webster Republican* published a detailed account of the January 8, 1897 wolf hunt, written by D. S. (Stoffer) Hamrick.

AUTHOR'S COMMENTARY

The year 1900 was a turning point in the long history of wildlife throughout the Appalachian Mountains and their associated watersheds. The buffalo (bison), elk, passenger pigeon, Carolina parakeet, heath hen, and timber wolf had been eliminated.

Several other species reached historical population lows at the turn of the century. Beaver, black bear, wild turkey, fisher, river otter, and white-tailed deer were so scarce that many feared they would follow the buffalo, elk, and timber wolf onto the pages of history. Fewer than 1,000 deer existed in all of West Virginia.

However, the 1900s brought a reversal in wildlife fortunes that no one could have predicted. Even some "new" species (i.e., coyote and wild boar) eventually became established. Many species adapted to humans, learning to tolerate and even benefit from their presence.

More than 100 years have passed since the last free-ranging timber wolf roamed the Appalachian Mountains. The prey base of white-tailed deer has exploded, resulting in irreparable damage to the forests and plant communities. Because of near optimum habitat and low numbers of wild predators, white-tailed deer are more abundant than ever, numbering in the tens of millions. Even free-ranging elk now occur at scattered locations throughout the Appalachians. River otters occur in many streams, and fishers hunt amidst the upland forests.

Wild turkey numbers have also rebounded and these majestic birds are abundant throughout the mountains. Large stands of red spruce once again blanket much of Cheat Mountain.

However, the ecosystems encompassing much of the central Appalachians are incomplete. There are inadequate numbers of predators at the top of the food chain. Admittedly, black bears and coyotes are common, and even an occasional mountain lion wanders the Appalachians. But the ecosystems remain strikingly unbalanced. Possibly mountain lions will rebound in numbers and coyotes will continue to increase, but bears, coyotes, and mountain lions will never be abundant enough to significantly reduce the deer herd. Only free-ranging packs of timber wolves could bring the ecosystems back into balance. But this will likely never happen. The key "predator" that hunts the forests and valleys of Appalachia, if only for a few selected weeks each fall and winter, is the alpha species that cannot tolerate the most similar foe it ever faced.

ABOUT THE AUTHOR

Dr. Michael is a native West Virginian. He was born on Plum Run, in Marion County, near Mannington and Farmington, attended elementary school in Shinnston, and graduated from Magnolia High School in New Martinsville. He received a B.S. degree in Biology from Marietta College, and M.S. and Ph.D. degrees in Wildlife Ecology from Texas A&M University. He taught at West Virginia University from 1970 through 1997. His 50-year career as a wildlife biologist produced more than 100 publications, both scientific and popular. Dr. Michael continues to be an active outdoorsman, researcher, and writer, concentrating his efforts on the wildlife of the Appalachian Mountains. Recent products of this writing included *Wild and Wonderful: The Wildlife of West Virginia*, *Death Visits Canaan*, *Shadow of the Alleghenies*, and *A Valley Called Canaan*.